TEACHING TAI CHI
EFFECTIVELY

Other publications by Dr Paul Lam

Available from Tai Chi Productions
6 Fisher Place, Narwee, NSW 2209, Australia
www.taichiproductions.com

Books

Tai Chi for Beginners and the 24 Forms, Paul Lam and Nancy Kaye
Overcoming Arthritis, Paul Lam and Judith Horstman

Instructional DVDs/Videos

Tai Chi for Arthritis (DVD available in English, Chinese, French, Spanish, German and Italian)

Tai Chi for Osteoporosis

Tai Chi for Diabetes

Tai Chi for Back Pain

Tai Chi for Older Adults

Tai Chi 4 Kidz

Tai Chi for Beginners (DVD available in English, Chinese, French, Spanish, German and Italian)

Qigong for Health

Tai Chi — the 24 Forms

The 32 Forms Tai Chi Sword

The Combined 42 Forms

The 42 Forms Tai Chi Sword

TEACHING TAI CHI EFFECTIVELY

Dr Paul Lam

Tai Chi Productions

First published in Australia in 2006 by Tai Chi Productions
6 Fisher Place, Narwee, NSW 2209, Australia
www.taichiproductions.com

The National Library of Australia
Cataloguing-in-Publication entry:

    Lam, Paul.
      Teaching tai chi effectively.

    ISBN 0 9752003 9 9.

    1. Tai chi - Study and teaching. I. Title.

    613.7148071

Designed and typset by Diana Cornwell
Cover design by Matthew Lam
Printed in Australia by Shannon Books

"All learning begins when our comfortable ideas turn out to be inadequate."

John Dewey
Educator and philosopher

About the author

Dr Paul Lam, a practising physician and tai chi master for 30 years, is a world leader in the field of tai chi for health improvement. In collaboration with other medical and tai chi experts, Dr Lam has created several Tai Chi for Health programs to help improve people's wellbeing and quality of life. His programs, Tai Chi for Arthritis, Tai Chi for Osteoporosis and Tai Chi for Diabetes are supported by the Arthritis Foundation of Australia; Osteoporosis Australia; Arthritis Foundation of the USA; Arthritis Care, UK; Korean Rheumatology Health Professionals Association; and Diabetes Australia.

With his authorised master trainers, Dr Lam has conducted hundreds of instructors' training workshops around the world for his Tai Chi for Health programs. In conjunction with other organisations and tai chi colleagues, Dr Lam has also presented a series of tai chi workshops for a comprehensive range of styles and forms, both in Australia and the USA.

Dr Lam is the founder and chief instructor of Better Health Tai Chi Chuan Inc (since 1986), a non profit-making organisation with the aim of providing an enjoyable and supportive environment for all its members to learn and to grow through tai chi chuan. In 1998, he founded the Tai Chi Association of Australia, an organisation that aims to bring tai chi enthusiasts together.

At the Third International Tai Chi Competition in Beijing (1993), Dr Lam won a gold medal for the Combined 42 Competition Forms, as well as two silver medals for the Combined 42 Tai Chi Sword Forms and the Chen Style Forms. Since then, he has been appointed the chief judge for several international competitions. Many of his students have competed successfully in international competition.

Graduating in 1974 from the medical school of the University of New South Wales, Australia, on a university scholarship, Dr Lam is a family physician in Sydney, Australia. He has been a clinical teacher with the Family Medicine Program for 20 years and is a lecturer at the University of NSW.

Dr Lam has produced many best-selling books, instructional videos and DVDs on the topic of tai chi and health. He has contributed to many medical research studies on tai chi and health in the capacity of chief investigator, co-author, consultant and adviser. Dr Lam has written and co-authored many published papers and articles for peer review medical journals and lay magazines. In addition, Dr. Lam has presented papers on the subject of tai chi for health at numerous national and international conferences. He is a keynote speaker for the first Tai Chi for Health International Conference in Seoul, Korea, in 2006.

Acknowledgments

Many people have contributed significantly to the development of this book, especially over the last five years, which has seen four major re-writes. It is impossible to name you all. Thank you to the thousands of tai chi friends, students and teachers who have inspired and supported me.

In particular, I'd like to thank my friend Nancy Kaye, whose support, editing and challenges have shaped this book and, later on, Diana Cornwell, for her driving force and marvellous editing that has helped me complete it. Special thanks also to Cheryl Lee Player for her wonderful illustrations for the book.

Among the many teaching colleagues and friends who have directly contributed to this book, I'd like to thank: Elva and Denis Arthy, Margaret Brade, Angela Cantafio, Maree Chadwick, Carol Cheung, John Chew, Dr Hyun Mi Cho, Georgette Coffey, Dr Janet Cromb, Ralph Dehner, Caroline Demoise, Dr Aeyong Eom, Ian Etcell, Barbara Foster, Sue Fry, Kam Lau Fung, Madelene Gavin, Edric Hong, Rani Hughes, Indria Jahja, Dan Jones, Julie King, Dr Pam Kircher, Wilfred Kwok, Pat Lawson, Professor Eunok Lee, Kwan and Sylvia Leung, Professor Vince McCullough, Charles Miller, John Mills, Jef Morris, Peter Ng, Rosemary Palmer, Joan Peters, Alan Pollocks, Peter Poon, Norman Precious, Paul Pritchard, Shelia Rae, Trevor J Reynaert, Leslie Roberts, Professor Russell Smiley, Jana Solovka, Professor Rhayun Song, Dr Stephanie Taylor, Professor Troyce Thome, Hazel Thompson, Jay Van Shelt, Charles Tsui-po, Toi Walker, Dennis Watts, Jackie Watts, Netta Watts, Pat Webber, Sybil Wong and Swee Yeo.

And a special thank you to all the people whose photos have added good energy to the book.

Thanks also to Dr Yanchy Lacska, Dr Stephanie Taylor, Pat Webber, Shelia Rae and Professor Russell Smiley for their kind permission to reprint their insightful articles about what it takes to be an effective teacher.

I'm especially grateful to the instructors and students of my tai chi school, Better Health Tai Chi Chuan Inc, my workshop manager, Anna Bennett, my USA director, Celia Liu, and all the staff of Tai Chi Productions, for their dedication to our tai chi vision and for making it possible for me to spend time on this book.

Finally, my love and gratitude go to my wife Eunice for her support and guidance, my daughter Andrea, who does not realise how much she has inspired me, and my son Matthew, for his genius in designing the book cover. Lastly my greatest gratitude is to my father-in-law Mr Frederick Lum — my first and most significant tai chi teacher — thank you for being such an open minded and caring teacher.

Contents

How this book can make you a more effective teacher

This book is designed to help both you and your students enjoy and develop your tai chi. The way you teach determines how much your students will learn and enjoy their tai chi. By teaching effectively, your students will learn well and enjoy their tai chi more, which will keep them coming back to your class. You will be more fulfilled as a teacher and at the same time will improve your own level of tai chi.

Margaret Brade, CEO of *Age Concern*, Stockport, UK, a tai chi teacher, says this of her own teacher: '…[he] had some magic for me — and many others. It is hard to capture in words what someone has that makes 30+ people turn up twice a week, week after week — all those instructors that have come after him (he has now retired) have not managed it and people still constantly talk of Bruce.'

I have worked with thousands of tai chi teachers over 30 years, many of them with Bruce's magic. I have collected and analysed the reasons behind their success and present them here for you. If you find just one idea in this book that assists you to help more students learn and benefit from tai chi, then it will have been worthwhile reading this book.

Kay has quite a different story to tell about her first teacher. I got to know Kay when she took my Tai Chi for Arthritis class. She explained to me that 10 years earlier she had decided to take up tai chi, thinking that it would be relaxing and helpful to her stressful lifestyle. Besides, she felt badly in need of regular exercise.

At her first lesson, a class for beginners, the teacher began the class with a long talk on the history of tai chi and the theories behind it — yin and yang and the five elements. He talked very fast in an effort to pass on so much information.

For the first few minutes, Kay was fascinated. But as the teacher went on, she began to feel perplexed, overwhelmed and finally confused. Was she relieved when the practice session began! In addition to her confusion, her arthritic knees had begun to ache from having to stand while the teacher talked — and talked.

Kay's relief was short-lived. The teacher taught only one thing in the entire lesson — a warm-up exercise. Nevertheless, Kay felt good about learning to swing both arms back and forth; good, that is, until the teacher came to her and pointed out the many things she was doing wrong. After that she felt clumsy.

At the end of the class, the teacher stressed to all the students that tai chi is a deep and sophisticated art. 'Don't expect to learn anything worthwhile for the first year', he told them, adding that if they weren't prepared to work diligently they should not come back.

Kay left her first class with the impression that tai chi was going to be very difficult for her to learn, and she was not thrilled about the prospect of working for a year without gaining anything worthwhile. Disillusioned, she didn't return, along with, I suspect, many of the other beginners.

It took several years before she decided to give it another try. That's when she came to one of the Tai Chi for Arthritis workshops and fell in love with tai chi. Since then, she has continued to learn, practise and later to teach tai chi. Through tai chi, she has helped her students improve their health and quality of life. And tai chi has helped her cope with several major challenges in her own life.

I've heard many stories similar to Kay's. If the students weren't discouraged by the perceived difficulty of the art, they were discouraged by the way their teachers taught it. I have met teachers like Kay's who are highly skilled tai chi practitioners, passionate about teaching but lacking the know-how to do it more effectively. This book will help them.

The core of the book is the teaching system I have developed from years of research and experience, the Stepwise Progressive Teaching Method. Over the last 20 years, I have shared the system in workshops I've conducted with thousands of tai chi teachers around the world. My student teachers consistently vote this method of teaching as the most useful segment of these workshops.

Dr Yanchy Lacska, from Minnesota, USA, an experienced tai chi and qigong teacher, describes the usefulness of my system when he says: 'As well as being a psychologist for 20 years, I have been an educator at the public school and university level for 32 years. The Stepwise Progressive Teaching Method is by far the most effective method for teaching physical skills that I have ever encountered.' He continues: 'I not only use this method to teach tai chi, but also in teaching qigong, crisis intervention and self defense workshops. Dr Lam's Stepwise teaching method has truly helped me become a better teacher and has made learning complex skills easier for my students.'

In this book I also include many useful ideas and practical methods for teaching tai chi. Throughout the book, I'll use real life examples to illustrate important points, which will help you take a better course of action as well as avoid obvious pitfalls. The stories are real but the names are changed to protect privacy. However, if I am quoting anyone I will provide their real names.

How to use this book

This book gives new and experienced tai chi teachers the theoretical background and practical methodology to teach tai chi effectively. It is designed to be read in the order presented and should be a valuable reference tool for many years. However, if you really need some quick assistance with your teaching you can read the introductions to each of the chapters in Part 1 and then go straight to Chapters 5 and 6 in Part 2, which contain the essence of my teaching method. If you do this though, be sure you come back later and read the rest of the book from the beginning, because my teaching method will then work more effectively for you. For those teachers who need urgent and step-by-step guidance, you'll find in Part 3 a sample lesson plan for the first three lessons. Remember though, that last minute 'quick fixes' won't work in the long run; be sure to start from the beginning of this book as soon as possible.

For experienced teachers, you're welcome to browse and pick topics of interest that may enhance your skills. I would suggest, however, that you still read the first two parts of this book to gain an overall picture as well as the rationale behind effective teaching.

Part 3: *Tools* covers a variety of topics that can be used as tools to help you become a more effective teacher and is designed for you to choose those topics that interest you.

I urge you to spend some time thinking about the methods and rationale of the system I have presented in this book. Visualise using these methods in a real life situation, then test them out and adapt them to your needs as appropriate. Try to practise them whenever you can: the art of teaching is like the art of tai chi, regular practice is a must for improvement. Keep checking on what works best for you so that you can continue to fine tune your teaching skills.

Working with people in a learning situation is a very challenging task. No two situations are exactly alike and there is no single solution for all situations. The key is to understand the rationale and the principles I have presented and integrate them into your own system of teaching. A single absolutely correct way for any situation is not possible. What is possible, is to keep working toward a better way.

On the other hand, working with people is also very rewarding. Empowering your students to find enjoyment and health through tai chi is most fulfilling. My book is dedicated to help you achieve these rewards faster and to have more enjoyment on the journey there.

PART 1: THE TEACHER

Why do so many of us teach tai chi? What are the rewards for us? What skills do we need to be a teacher? How do we know that we are teaching effectively? In this part of the book I will attempt to provide answers to these questions, with the aim of helping you understand how you can improve your efficiency as a teacher, rather than setting any hard and fast rules or standards.

I always wanted to be a teacher. It's in my blood. My late father was a great teacher and even though I practise medicine, I don't just treat people; I also teach. I train new doctors before they go out on their own and I teach medical and health science students, doctors, physiotherapists and other health professionals, as well as people from many other walks of life. And, of course, I teach tai chi. I teach tai chi to people at all levels, from beginners to international competitors. I love teaching and enjoy learning how to do it better.

There are hundreds of good tai chi books available today, but so far, none on teaching it. Yet, for tai chi to grow and progress, effective teaching is the most important factor.

For years, I have been training teachers to run my Tai Chi for Health programs. In my workshops, I have incorporated structured teaching sessions to enable effective learning. Many teachers have told me how useful they have found them. After learning my Tai Chi for Arthritis program from one of my workshops, Evelyn, a physiotherapist from Switzerland, started teaching it. Soon she was running several classes and had a waiting list of students, while more experienced tai chi teachers running classes nearby had problems attracting enough students. Many instructors of my programs have told me of similar experiences. I want to share these effective methods with more tai chi teachers so that together we can reach and help more people. Tai chi teachers are not competing in a limited market. If we have more effective teachers it will simply bring more students to all of us and, what is more, it will introduce more people to tai chi and a healthier and happier life.

Realising that the progress of our society depends on knowledge being passed down from teacher to student, I've gradually increased the amount of time I spend teaching. For me, the journey to be a more effective teacher has been challenging, even frustrating at times, but in the end, immensely rewarding. I really enjoy discovering new ways to improve my teaching skills. I have discovered also that teaching tai chi improves my tai chi skills as well as my inter-personal skills.

It wasn't always this way, though. The traditionalists placed heavy emphasis on tai chi skills in teaching tai chi. According to tai chi tradition, a student had to be in training full time for many years before they could reach a level high enough to become a teacher. Actually, most of the traditionalists didn't even consider teaching as a skill in itself.

When I started teaching, I'd received no instruction from my own teachers on how to teach. I simply began by following their methods of teaching. In those early years I was particularly focused on picking up my student's mistakes. I'd stand on the stage and ask my students to practise in a group. Then, starting with the more talented students, I'd pick up on many of their mistakes, mimicking them one by one, pointing out who did this and who did that, and telling them how it should be done. The more talented a student was, the more I picked on them, because I thought they had the most potential for growth. Praise was a rare commodity: I was too busy looking for mistakes.

People used to tell me how incredible it was that I was able to remember so many points at one time. I took that as positive feedback. In retrospect, it is a surprise that any of those students stayed with me — that they did is probably because, despite my poor teaching, they knew that my passion for tai chi and respect for them was genuine. As I improved my teaching skills, I noticed that more students were coming back, were learning more quickly and, most importantly, were getting more enjoyment out of their tai chi. And just as importantly, I was enjoying teaching more too.

Chapter 1
Why teach tai chi?

I teach tai chi mostly because I enjoy doing it. When I teach, I am often completely absorbed. I feel truly alive; my mind and body work at their best and time loses its limitation on me. Teaching tai chi puts me in the 'flow' stage and I enjoy these experiences so much I want to teach more. Teaching tai chi has changed my life very significantly: I have learned so much about teaching and about people and have improved my own tai chi and health beyond my dreams.

I am proud that I have helped so many people improve their health and quality of life through tai chi. A wonderful example of this is Cheryl, a nurse from Canada, who suffers from fibromyalgia, a condition that causes tiredness, pain and stiffness and has no known cure. Cheryl was so badly affected that she had to give up her part-time job and employ a nanny to take care of her young children. After six months of Tai Chi for Arthritis, Cheryl had improved to the point that she was able to care for her own children and go back to her job.

> *"I've met countless teachers who tell me how happy they are that they are helping to improve their students' health."*

Dr Pam Kircher, in her book *Love is the link*[1], says: 'When we understand that we are here (in this lifetime) to learn to be more loving, we will require fewer physical objects and will prefer life-enhancing activities... Our own interests will no longer be more paramount to us than the interest of our neighbors.' If we believe, like Pam, that our purpose in life is to learn to love and to help others, then teaching tai chi is a great way to enhance our lives. I've met countless teachers who tell me how happy they are that they are helping to improve their students' health.

True, it is not always an easy journey. When you know the difficulties and the frustrations that we tai chi teachers sometimes go through, it's amazing that there are still so many of us. Sometimes we spend a lot of time and energy teaching, with little obvious result. And, of course, many tai chi teachers gain very little, if any, financial reward for all their efforts.

In my workshops around the world, I've asked thousands of tai chi teachers why they teach. It hasn't come as any surprise to me to find that teachers from different countries and backgrounds give similar answers:

- Helping people improve their health.
- Helping people with arthritis, diabetes or other chronic conditions improve their particular conditions and the quality of their lives.
- Helping people develop patience, tranquility and inner balance.
- Sharing their own love of the art of tai chi.
- Enjoying teaching.
- Improving their own tai chi skills through teaching.
- Filling the need for tai chi teachers.
- Enjoying being part of the tai chi family.

Many people have multiple reasons for teaching tai chi. Like Margaret's teacher Bruce, of whom she says: 'It was clear at all times that his focus was on sharing his love and enthusiasm for tai chi. He was also committed to and totally convinced that tai chi was beneficial to health and he passed that on to everyone.'

Helping people improve their health

It is human nature to want to heal others, and so it gives many tai chi teachers a great sense of fulfilment when they are able to improve people's health, using such a safe form of therapy as tai chi.

More and more studies are showing how effective tai chi is in improving many aspects of health[2], and how much this could save in terms of health costs. If we look at one example of the health benefits of tai chi, prevention of falling — that contribution alone could save the US economy in excess of $10 billion[3] and the Australian economy more than $400 million[4] each year. If we were to add up all the health benefits from tai chi, the health cost savings would be astronomical. No one can put a price on better health and quality of life, but money saved can be put to better use. For tai chi teachers the end result — making a positive difference to people's lives — is very fulfilling. That's something money can't buy.

Helping your students to develop tranquillity and inner balance

Tai chi allows you to express both your mind and your body. By creating a positive and encouraging atmosphere in your classes, your students will feel comfortable expressing their inner selves. By helping your students to learn how to express and appreciate themselves, you will be helping them achieve much more than just learning tai chi and improving their health — you will also be helping them become more harmonised. That's a powerful form of therapy. Jef Morris says: 'In tai chi, we create a place where people can be themselves, feel safe to express themselves as they are, safe from being criticized. They will learn to find their own value and to love themselves better…' Only when we truly value and love ourselves can we value and love others.

> *"By helping your students to learn how to express and appreciate themselves, you will be helping them achieve much more than just learning tai chi and improving their physical health…"*

Improving your own skills

For many people, improving their own tai chi skills is a strong reason for teaching tai chi. Teaching helps you to gain a deeper understanding of the art. You have to break down the movements, analyse all the parts and understand the overall picture in order to teach well. This forces you to look at the detail of different aspects of a form and beyond its superficial appearance. My friend Janet told me, after a week of intensive teaching at our annual workshop, 'I've learned so much from my students. They [the students] were surprised to hear that I've learned a lot more from them than they have from me.'

It's true. Teachers can learn a lot from their students, not just from their challenging questions, but also from their input and stimulation. Sometimes, when faced with challenging questions, we come up with excellent answers that we are not aware that we are capable of. Students stimulate us to think more deeply and thinking helps us grow in knowledge and skill. When I am fully absorbed in my teaching, I am in the 'flow'. My mind works at its best, and my technique improves in quantum leaps.

Filling the need for tai chi teachers

As tai chi becomes more popular, teachers are in greater demand. Take Ray, for example. Ray lives in a small, isolated town in the centre of Australia and learned tai chi from a book. One day, as he was practising tai chi in a park, some people saw him and were so intrigued that they asked him to teach them. Although he told them that he wasn't all that experienced, they insisted and, since there was no other teacher in the area, Ray took on the job. Before long he had a loyal group of students.

Enjoying the feeling of belonging to the tai chi family

A sense of belonging is a powerful incentive to teach tai chi. Unlike the family we're connected to by birth, members of the tai chi family have chosen each other. I really enjoy spending time with my tai chi family. Many of my students regard their tai chi associates as an extended family and, during challenging times, they find strength and support from each other.

Passing on your love and enthusiasm for the art of tai chi

Tai chi teachers love to share their art with other people. Teaching is giving and we love to give and, in giving, we receive so much back in return.

Chapter 2
What it takes to be an effective teacher

Professor Rhayun Song of Chungnam National University in Korea and a master trainer of the Tai Chi for Health programs, summed it up very well: 'The inexperienced teachers teach from the book; the more experienced teachers teach what they know and the most experienced teachers teach what students need to learn.' The effectiveness of a teacher is measured by how successfully they meet their students' needs. The important thing to remember is that the more student-orientated you are, the more successful you will be and the more you will enjoy your teaching. Once you know the route you must take, you can become one of these 'most experienced' teachers in a short time.

Three attributes measure your effectiveness as a tai chi teacher: your attitude, your tai chi skills and your teaching skills. In Chapter 5 *The Stepwise Progressive Teaching Method* these will be incorporated into one easy-to-learn system.

> *"The effectiveness of a teacher is measured by how successfully they meet their students' needs."*

An effective teacher will motivate and inspire their students to enjoy and practise their tai chi. If your students don't enjoy their tai chi they will soon stop practising and, without practice, they will not improve their technique or gain any of the benefits, no matter how brilliant they are. Your right attitude will motivate and inspire your students.

Students have different objectives; therefore different levels of skill are required to teach them. For example, teaching tai chi to older people for fall prevention would require a different set of skills than would be necessary to teach it as a martial art. Barbara, a physiotherapist from Tasmania, Australia, after taking a Tai Chi for Arthritis training workshop, has now taught the program to 112 people. Her students have reduced their number of falls by approximately half, as well as improving their balance, strength, ability to relax and self-confidence. Her results are as good, if not better, than most experienced tai chi teachers achieve. The same impressive results were shown by other scientific studies[1] with teachers trained at a similar two-day Tai Chi for Arthritis workshop[2].

Being proficient at tai chi is important in teaching tai chi but it does not necessarily make you a good teacher. Teaching is itself an art. As we saw from our story earlier about Evelyn, from Switzerland, her classes are more popular than those of a more experienced teacher nearby. What's more she gets better results.

When you teach tai chi, it is vitally important that you make sure your students learn it in safety, no matter what objectives they may have. Any injury they sustain will impede their progress towards their objective. Effective teachers understand about risk management and make sure that they minimise risk when teaching tai chi. For example, a straight-leg toe touch has a high risk of injury and a lower risk alternative should be used[3]. Chapter 4: *Safety first* is devoted to this topic.

No one becomes a great teacher without experience; but you will not gain this experience if you never start. I would like to encourage you to start teaching as soon as possible and learn as you go. It's not possible or even desirable to learn everything there is to learn about teaching before you start; it is much better for you to begin teaching when you have the basic skills necessary for the job and then improve your skills as you go.

Your attitude

Your attitude towards teaching tai chi and your students has three components to it:

1. Your passion for tai chi
2. Your relationship with your students
3. Being positive

Your passion for tai chi

When you are passionate about teaching tai chi, your students will know and respond to it. It is most important that your heart is in the right place, but passion alone will not be enough: just because you care about tai chi does not mean you will do a good job of teaching it. However, true passion will drive you to learn how to do it well.

Enthusiasm is contagious. In the long run though, students will keep coming to tai chi for their own reasons — enjoyment, health benefits and personal fulfilment. Your enthusiasm for tai chi provides a great kick-start, giving you time to bring these intrinsic rewards to your students. We have found that the first three months is a critical time. By the end of the third month, most students will gain significant health benefits and get over the initial awkwardness of learning something so different from traditional Western exercise. If you can keep your students for that period of time, they will be likely to stay with you.

> *"When you are passionate about teaching tai chi, your students will know and respond to it."*

On the other hand, over-enthusiasm can be off-putting for new pupils. Certainly be friendly and encouraging, but don't expect everyone to instantly fall in love with tai chi. Remember that many people have never tried anything like tai chi before and can be frustrated by the slowness of the movements. Especially for the elderly or physically challenged, tackling something new, particularly in a room full of strangers, can be daunting, and it is much more important to establish a warm, relaxed relationship than try to make people fall in love with tai chi.

Your relationship with your students

Mary Kay Ash, one of America's legendary business women and founder of the giant Mary Kay cosmetics company, is frequently quoted as saying: 'People don't care how much you know until they know how much you care.' Your caring attitude is important for your relationship with your students. Be like Jay who, despite lacking experience as a teacher, had good tai chi skills and a very caring attitude: as a result, in the end, he won over his students.

Some teachers like to use the so-called 'traditional model'. This model is often associated with an attitude that the teacher is superior and always right. Students of these teachers are not encouraged to think for themselves, but just to do what they are told. These teachers forbid their students to experience other teachers and demand total obedience. These teachers also often ignore any new developments, including improved safety precautions and teaching methods. This is not to say all traditionally trained teachers belong to this so-called 'traditional model'. There are traditionally trained teachers who are 'progressive' in their teaching.

Dot once told me about her traditional teacher, Mr Lee. Dot bought my instructional DVD to pick up a few extra ideas from it. As soon as Mr Lee found this out, he told her off in front of all the students and expelled her from his class. This is a narrow minded and unreasonable way to act in this present day and age.

Norman had a different experience. He came to my Tai Chi for Arthritis instructors' training workshop and his teacher Glen, who is more 'traditional' in his teaching style, was not happy about it. Norman talked with Glen, explaining that he was not being disloyal. In fact, he has learnt a new skill that could benefit both of them. Norman made an arrangement to set up his own Tai Chi for Arthritis class, at the same time working with Glen to promote his traditional Yang-style class. They collaborated through cross-referral and joint advertising. The end result is Glen still has Norman as a loyal student and both of their classes are expanding. Advanced students in Norman's class move into Glen's and Glen refers people with a disability to Norman's class. Just as importantly, both teachers are getting more enjoyment from their teaching and a greater number of students are benefiting from this.

In comparison to the traditional style, the modern style of teaching, the coaching approach[4], has many advantages. In this model, teachers work with students to help them reach their goals. The end result — how much the students have learnt and enjoyed the learning process — is by far superior and teachers are more fulfilled and retain more students. Learning in a relaxed, interactive and positive relationship is more effective.

Pat Webber, an effective teacher, says: 'Having had personal experiences of poor teaching in the past, experiences that have killed my initial interest in a number of subjects, has made me aware of the old saying, "Do unto others as you would have them do unto you".' What would you prefer? Being a slave to your teacher or learning in a positive environment? You can read Pat's article 'Do unto others…' in full in Chapter 12.

> *"Learning in a relaxed, interactive and positive relationship is more effective."*

This is not to say the traditional method is all bad: I have incorporated some parts of the traditional approach that work well into my teaching system.

A confident attitude is crucial for building a good relationship with your students. The confident teacher is not an arrogant teacher who has the air of knowing everything. Quite the opposite, a confident teacher is a person who is comfortable with their ability to teach, but also understands that no one can know everything and is always open to new ideas. I have found that the most effective teachers are friendly and approachable, no matter how important are their positions and how great their skills. I remember the first time I met Professor Vince McCullough in one of my workshops. He was a most friendly, approachable and eager to learn person. Later I found out how famous and experienced he is in teaching and in tai chi. Professor Vince McCullough is one of the most confident and effective teachers I have ever known.

Being positive

Being positive is a vital part of achieving the right attitude and of effective teaching. Being positive starts from the very beginning. Even before you start face to face teaching, as you prepare for your lessons, expect to succeed and you will have a better chance of doing so.

Thinking positively is contagious. Soon your students will feel the positive spirit and join you in making your lessons a success. If you expect your students to do well, the chances are better that they will. There is an interesting real life story about a mix up of IQ tests in a grade ten class. The results of one girl, who was thought to be third best in the class, were unintentionally mixed up with the results of another girl, who was near the bottom of the class. All the teachers, parents and both students were told of these (wrong) results, so everyone expected the girl who they were told had the higher IQ score to achieve good results. And at the end of the year, this girl did what everyone expected — she actually got third place. Meanwhile, the girl who should have achieved top marks, because she really had the higher IQ, came near the bottom of the class. In other words, they performed as they and everyone else expected them to do. Look around you and you may be able to find similar examples.

Giving positive feedback

Giving appropriate positive feedback is the single most important factor for effective teaching. Most people feel uncomfortable, or even insecure about learning something new, especially tai chi, which is very different from traditional Western exercise. When people feel uncomfortable, their minds are more inhibited and they learn more slowly. Giving appropriate positive feedback to your students improves their confidence and helps them to learn more quickly. This sets up a positive cycle of more confidence enhancing good performance, and good performance leading to more positive reinforcement, which in turn leads to more confidence. Do you remember an occasion when your teacher or parent told you had done something well? Did it make you feel good about your ability? Have you been doing that something much better ever since? Does it still make you enjoy that task more?

> *"Giving appropriate positive feedback is the single most important factor for effective teaching."*

In contrast, criticism and over correction often makes students feel inadequate, causing them to shrink back into their 'personal shell', closing their mind, and becoming less able to learn. (I will explain the mechanism of 'personal shell' later in this chapter.)

Positive feedback must, however, be meaningful and appropriate, otherwise it could have the opposite effect. For example, saying your student's movements are good because they are smooth is meaningful; just saying they are good is not meaningful. Positive feedback should be based on observation and be expressed appropriately: paying lip service does not work — if you have not observed your student's movement, you should not give feedback on it.

Hazel Thompson, an effective teacher from New Zealand, told me: 'I tried to give everyone some positive feedback. One elderly student had not shown any improvement in his tai chi skill, so I praised him about his improved balance.'

Be aware that the appropriateness of feedback is as perceived by your students. It is important that you take the time to get to know your students and find out what is appropriate for them. For example, to a very shy student, a loud comment on how great he or she is could be embarrassing or even be perceived as a sarcastic remark. A quiet word, 'Very nice — I like your gentle movements' when you are near that student may work better. For students who come from a culture such as Chinese, where praise is a rarity, open praise can be too overwhelming. Sometimes I find my Chinese students become genuinely embarrassed with strong positive feedback. More subtle feedback, like a smile or a nod is more appropriate in these cases.

Margaret says this about her teacher Bruce: 'He was very encouraging — never critical — always said if you didn't get it right or got lost, "smile" and then we did it right! He would give little signs of approval — often a nod or a smile at you if you did it particularly well. He would also ask a student to lead the class occasionally as recognition of their doing it well. When that happened to me for the first time I felt great!'

It is human nature to be critical. Many teachers have told me that they have no trouble finding many mistakes from their students, but to find good points is much more challenging. To give positive feedback well, you must orientate your mindset right from the start and make a conscious effort to look for the positives. Starting with yourself, do a positive self-appraisal and look for your own good points. When you catch yourself being over critical of yourself, substitute a positive thought for the critical one. Only when you are able to see yourself positively can you truly be able to view others positively. People with self-confidence inspire confidence in others. Professor Vince McCullough is a good example of someone who always inspires people around him with his self-confidence.

Correcting student's mistakes

The most common error I find in inexperienced teachers is that they try to correct too many mistakes. Often I watch an enthusiastic teacher hovering over a new student, giving them many detailed instructions and correcting several mistakes. Some even move the student's arms and legs to the desirable position. I recommend you do not do this: touching your students could lead to serious consequences for both you and the student. The student may have a medical condition, such as a strained ligament or inflamed joints, which could be aggravated by someone trying to move the part unexpectedly. Also, in this litigious age, it can be dangerous for you to touch a student, as you could be accused of causing injury or touching inappropriately.

> "The most common error I find in inexperienced teachers is that they try to correct too many mistakes."

Hazel seldom singles out any one student for correction. If she sees a mistake, especially one made by several students, she goes through the correction with the whole class. If any of the students still do not get it right, she either tries to demonstrate it in a different way — again with the entire class and without identifying the individual student — or she just lets it go. Unless you have an exceptional reason, it is better not to single out anyone for correction.

Most students find it overwhelming if they're given a lot of corrections at the same time. When they are overwhelmed they feel inadequate, lose their confidence, and their learning capacity is inhibited. As a rule of thumb, never give more than one correction at one time. Your students will learn more quickly when they only have to deal with one point at a time. Our brain is designed to be most efficient at handling one task at a time: multi-tasking sounds good but studies have shown it is less efficient than concentrating on one thing at a time.

A good way of being positive when correcting mistakes is, instead of thinking that your student is doing something wrong, think of it as a point for improvement. Instead of saying to students, 'No, that is a mistake, don't do it that way', say to them 'Try doing it this way. It may work better because of this reason'. Remember, there is seldom an absolute right or wrong way of doing something; rather, there are better ways to do it. If you give your students a relevant and understandable reason why they should do something differently they will learn more quickly.

An effective way to correct mistakes is to identify the most important and commonly committed mistake, then explain and demonstrate your point to the entire class. Be sure to explain why your way is better, and demonstrate clearly the original and the better way. Ask your students to follow you as you do it the better way, then check to ensure it has been done correctly. I will discuss this method further in Part 2 of this book.

Expecting success

Being positive means expecting good results from your students. I have worked with many people who have moved their performance up to a new level just because their teachers expected them to.

Kerry had been studying tai chi with her first teacher for ten years, but her teacher always expected her to be average and so she stayed at that level. When she joined my class, I recognised her ability and, without knowing anything about her previous teacher, simply expected her to do well. Somehow my expectation was passed on to her without words and her improvement has been phenomenal over the last three years. She told me that she has learned more over the last three years than in the previous ten years.

Speaking positively

Speaking positively creates an encouraging atmosphere, helping your students to let go of their fear of being inadequate. Many people are so worried about their perceived clumsiness that they will not try tai chi. When people like this pluck up enough courage to try tai chi, we should encourage them, not deter them, as Kay was deterred by her teacher.

Using positive language enhances learning, while negative language hinders. For example, 'remember' is positive while 'don't forget' is negative. Asking students to 'remember' to centre is more effective than saying 'don't forget' to centre. One day I overheard one teacher saying to her student: 'Now take a step forward, don't lean to one side, no, no, don't look down, no, no, no, don't step with the ball of your foot; don't hold your hand tight; don't lift up your elbow...' 'No' and 'don't' are words to avoid as much as possible. Substitute them with something positive like this: 'Take a step forward, keep your body upright; good, look ahead; keep your elbow relaxed. Yes, you are doing well.' If you ever catch yourself talking like the first person, try and change to the latter style and watch your students grow in confidence and skill.

> *"Tai Chi is a mind/body exercise and your positive energy will be expressed in your teaching."*

Using your positive spirit/energy

Tai chi is a mind/body exercise and your positive energy will be expressed in your teaching. The way you teach and do your tai chi forms often reveals your inner spirit.

Margaret Brade of *Age Concern*, Stockport, England, says this about my teaching: '...the positive "energy" you create around your teaching — it is a tangible demonstration of the positive power of good chi (qi)! I always come away from a session with you with renewed confidence and a desire to continue to learn more.'

Tai chi skills

How good your tai chi needs to be depends on your students' needs. If, for example, you're teaching tai chi to a group of elderly people for health improvement, a knowledge of how to work safely with older people is more important than having a high level of skill in tai chi.

An ability to do a simple set, such as the 12 movement Tai Chi for Arthritis program, would be sufficient to teach these students. Leslie has taught a class in a retirement village for many years. His students' average age is 80, and both Leslie and his students enjoy their tai chi class. Leslie never needs to call on the more advanced tai chi skills that he has spent many years learning; in fact he seldom uses more than half of the 12 movements with these students.

An effective teacher does not necessarily have to be a better performer of the exercise or sport than their students. For example, there are many top tennis coaches who have never reached the same level as the player they are coaching. Tai chi teachers do not necessarily have to be better at tai chi than their students in order to help them reach their objectives, but a higher level of tai chi will enhance their ability to do so.

> *"How good your tai chi needs to be depends on your students' needs."*

The art of good teaching has many principles that hold true, regardless of what is being taught. In one case that was studied in the field of academic teaching, a teacher who got poor results with his class complained that it was the boring topic he had to teach. An effective teacher, who had no prior knowledge of this topic, studied it overnight, took over the class and still got the same impressive results that he did with his own class. This study tells me that the topic and the depth of the knowledge are not the most important ingredients for effective teaching.

Having a higher level of skill at tai chi is an advantage. However, sometimes when a teacher is too advanced, they forget what it's like to be a beginner and become impatient with their students' progress. I have met many effective teachers with only basic tai chi skills, but hardly any effective teachers who have high level tai chi skills but poor teaching skills.

One high level instructor yelled at the top of her voice to a student she saw moving toward the door, 'Don't you dare leave in the middle of my class!' The student replied meekly, 'It is chilly, I was just trying to close the door.' Do you think this teacher (if she can keep her students) will get good results? Would you feel comfortable to be in her class?

Sometimes people who learn tai chi slowly do not feel so confident of their tai chi skills and are less inclined to want to teach it. The fact is that the slow learners have to work harder to learn, so they probably can appreciate the average learner better. I often find they turn out to be better teachers than many fast learners.

As a rough guide, I suggest that the following are the appropriate levels of tai chi skill required to teach students at different levels. However, these are not hard and fast rules.

A: Beginners — Students' objectives are to maintain or improve mental and physical health, to learn tai chi as an exercise, as an art or for self-growth.

To teach beginners, it is desirable that you:

- Be proficient at leading appropriate warm-up and cooling-down exercises.
- Understand how to teach safely and how to adapt exercises for people with different kinds of physical abilities. For example, for people who cannot kick out one foot, you could change it to stepping forward[5].
- Be able to perform a recognisable set of tai chi movements with a basic level of understanding of the essential tai chi principles. For example, the teacher of the Tai Chi for Arthritis program should be able to perform the 12 movements well and apply the six essential tai chi principles for beginners[6].
- Be willing to continue to learn (with a teacher or teaching material such as an instructional DVD), and able to use the essential principles for continual progression.
- Be familiar with a brief history of tai chi, including knowing that there are many forms of tai chi, and be familiar with the major characteristics of at least two main styles.

B: Intermediate — Students' objectives are to gain more skill, knowledge and health benefits from their tai chi. They are enthusiastic about tai chi and willing to commit more time and energy to develop their tai chi skill. Students may reach this stage after approximately one year of tai chi experience.

It is desirable for those who teach this level to have all of the above requirements for teaching beginners and also:

- Be proficient in a set of forms, such as the 24 Forms, to a reasonable standard as accepted by the peers of your style.
- Understand the essential principles of tai chi to an intermediate level, and how to incorporate these principles into the forms.
- Know the history and development of tai chi, and the major characteristics of the four main styles.
- Practise tai chi regularly.

C: Advanced — Students' objectives are to explore the higher levels of tai chi and incorporate many of the tai chi principles into their daily lives. For example, living a more balanced lifestyle and learning how to relax. Students could reach this level after two or more years of tai chi experience. Students show a commitment to tai chi practice; some of them could already be a tai chi teacher or assistant teacher.

Tai chi has infinite depth. Within the art there are different directions for advanced students to move into, such as health, personal growth and martial arts. Advanced students should know which direction they wish to develop and should be able to choose a teacher who is proficient at teaching students in that direction.

> *"A good teacher does not necessarily need to have more internal power, a stronger stance, or be able to fight better than their students."*

A good teacher does not necessarily need to have more internal power, a stronger stance, or be able to fight better than their students. A good teacher should have the skills outlined above and any additional skills necessary for their students' area of special interest. The teacher should know how to identify their students' strong and weak points and be able to guide them to develop their skills. The teacher must have the ability to effectively demonstrate the skill (like a tennis coach explaining and demonstrating a better backhand drive). Having a high level of experience, knowledge and skill in tai chi are all helpful in becoming a teacher of advanced students.

Teaching skills

Teaching is both a science and an art. There is a wealth of knowledge about effective teaching methods in different fields and new research is expanding our knowledge every day. Also, with the development of new teaching aids, there are more and different approaches to effective teaching. For example, multi-media communication tools like DVDs have revolutionised the learning and teaching process. No one knows everything there is to know about teaching, but then you don't need to know everything to be effective.

There are three desirable teaching skills. In Chapter 5, *The Stepwise Progressive Teaching Method*, I will incorporate all these skills into a practical and easy-to-learn system.

The three desirable teaching skills are:
1.   Teaching the learner's way.
2.   Communicating effectively.
3.   Facilitating enjoyment.

Teaching the learner's way

Teaching in the way that learners learn best is the key to effective teaching. Try to put yourself in a learner's shoes, and ask yourself how would you like to be taught. It helps to have an understanding of how people learn, as there are different types of learners. Some will respond better to one way of teaching and others to another way of teaching. When teaching a group, use the method that works for as many different types of learners as possible.

> *"Teaching in the way that learners learn best is the key to effective teaching."*

Dr Jason Chang, PhD, a teacher from the University of Arkansas, describes teaching as being like radio broadcasting — students have different wavelengths and you must tune your teaching to their frequency. You need to find out what wavelength your students are on, then you can get through to your students. Finding ways to work with different learners is like tuning in to your students' wavelengths. For example, using spoken instructions only may work well for a group of auditory learners, but if you also have visual learners in the group, to be effective, you will need to teach with movement as well.

Different types of learners

There are no right or wrong styles of learning, but students will learn better when taught in a certain way, depending on the type of learner they are.

Most people are a mixture of learning types, though some are predominantly one type. Understanding these different types of learning will help you teach your students more effectively.

There are different ways to classify types of learners. Below are the three main types of learners, as based on the best known classification.

> *"There are no right or wrong styles of learning, but students will learn better when taught in a certain way, depending on the type of learner they are."*

1. Visual learners

These people learn best by watching how it's done. People from Western cultures are more likely to be visual learners. Children are also much more likely to be visual learners. Giving demonstrations, and showing pictures or diagrams can be very useful. For example, in teaching the Tai Chi for Diabetes forms, people tend to be confused with the direction they should move. I have found that by drawing a simple flow chart on the board it helps students to remember the sequence. An example of a flow chart, for the Tai Chi for Diabetes forms is shown on the next page.

I have tried teaching the sequence with and without this flow chart and have been amazed at how much more quickly most people learn with it than without it.

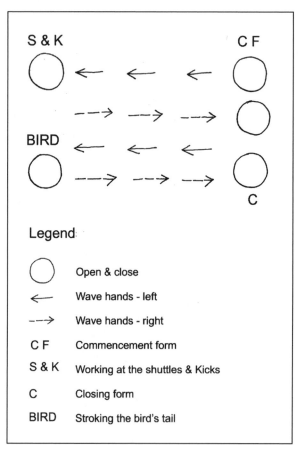

Chart 1: Flow chart for Tai Chi for Diabetes forms

2. Auditory learners

These people learn best by hearing things told to them, so, to help this type of student learn, a tai chi teacher should give them regular voice cues and talk out the instructions as they demonstrate the moves. Encourage your auditory students to talk the movements out to themselves as they are learning them. It is important that your instructions are simple, clear and to the point: people often get confused if you use too many complicated words, or give too many instructions at once. Remember though to provide some quiet time for other types of learners as well.

3. Kinaesthetic learners

Kinaesthetic learners learn best by doing it. If you talk too much you may find these people becoming jittery and impatient. Kinaesthetic learners often move their bodies as they listen, and appear restless when you are talking too much. These are the 'hands-on learners' or the 'doers' who concentrate better and learn more easily when movement is involved. Therefore getting students to follow you and demonstrate the movement back to you is helpful.

There are other ways of classifying learners that overlap the three discussed above and have a different emphasis. For example, other classifications may include very contrasting types such as:

Active learners and reflective learners

Active learners are nearly the same as kinaesthetic learners. These people learn best by doing things. This works well with tai chi, as it is an art that involves activity. Talking about tai chi without practising it will never make you a good tai chi practitioner, nor will it deliver as much benefit. In the earlier example about Kay's first teacher, an active learner would have been very frustrated having to listen to a half hour talk before any actual tai chi was done. When you teach a movement, get your students to try it with you and then repeat it. I will show you how this system works in more detail in Chapter 5: *The Stepwise Progressive Teaching Method*. There are more active learners than reflective learners.

Reflective learners prefer to think about information before they use it. When you teach tai chi, you will sometimes encounter people who just want to sit there and think about what you've told them, or go to a corner and work it out themselves. Be aware of this and structure your teaching to allow it. During a workshop I gave once in Sweden, I was having problems teaching one particular movement. I taught it the best I could and some students still couldn't seem to get it. I stopped instructing them, asked the class to work by themselves for a while and went outside to get a drink. I was pleasantly surprised when I came back a few minutes later to find everyone now knew the movement well. There must have been a few reflective learners in that group.

Remember the teacher who yelled at the meek student who was just trying to close the door? The same teacher also yelled loudly at one reflective learner who had gone quietly to the back of the class to try and work out how to do the movement. Yelling is not an effective way to communicate.

Sequential learners and global learners

Some people learn best by doing things in a logical order of progression, learning as they go. This works well with tai chi because it is designed as a progression of forms. Teaching the tai chi set in the right order is effective. Eugene, believing it to be a useful challenge for his students, teaches the forms in a random order, that is, Form 1 and then Form 5, then back to Form 3, and then Form 7, and later linking them all together in the correct order. This is creating barriers rather than facilitating learning. For most students, it is easier to learn the forms in their designed sequence. I imagine Eugene's challenge would drive his sequential learners crazy.

> *"Our brains and bodies are programmed to learn more effectively if we approach new tasks, one step at a time."*

Global learners are people who need to see the full picture before they can learn something well and sometimes they don't need to have things taught to them in a sequence. Eugene is probably a global learner and he assumes everyone will learn the same way as he does. For a while, the global learners may not understand what you're explaining to them, but then a critical piece of information arrives and everything falls into place for them. For these learners, a demonstration of the entire movement is helpful before they begin to do it themselves. I often hear students exclaiming 'I've got it!' after finally understanding one piece of information — the global learner has just got that missing piece!

There are more sequential learners than global learners. The *Stepwise Progressive Teaching Method* works well for both these types of learner.

One step at a time

Our brains and bodies are programmed to learn more effectively if we approach new tasks, one step at a time. This is especially true for tai chi, since there are so many steps within each movement. In the long run, teaching one step at a time enables all learners to learn more effectively. If you jump any of these steps, you may learn faster but you will miss out on some of the details and important underlying principles.

Sometimes it is important to stimulate your students' thinking. You can do this, by teaching one step at a time and letting your students practise and work things out themselves before you move on to the next step. Give them time to work out what comes next instead of offering them cues all the time. Students need time to think and to absorb: teaching too much, too quickly, can be counter-productive. The *Stepwise Progressive Teaching Method* in Chapter 5 takes this into account.

Working with the plateau phase

In his book *Mastery*[7], George Leonard, a well-known Californian martial arts expert, describes the 'plateau phase'. He explains that learners go through phases. In between each steep improvement, there's a long plateau phase, where improvement is slow and not so obvious. This phase is necessary for absorbing knowledge and honing skills before the next phase of rapid advancement can happen. Chart 2 gives an example of a learning curve, showing steep rises with plateaus in between.

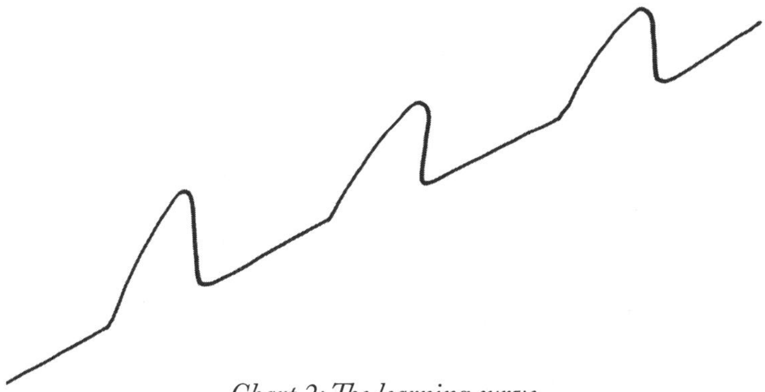

Chart 2: The learning curve

Impatient students become bored and disappointed during the plateau phase and often drop out. These people will miss out on the enoyment of achieving proficiency in tai chi and gaining its full benefits.

I will discuss the concept of 'enhancing flow' later in this chapter, to help you bring more enjoyment to your students when they are going through these plateau phases. In tai chi, plateaus and steep learning rises are yin and yang: during plateaus you are storing energy and during the rises you are delivering energy. You need to store energy before you have the energy to deliver it. In the long run, being aware of and learning how to enjoy the plateaus will help you stay with and make greater progress in tai chi. Sybil Wong, senior instructor from my school, *Better Health Tai Chi Chuan*, says after she finds she's reached a plateau, she simply focuses on enjoying the practice and doesn't think about advancing her skills, then when this happens, she is pleasantly surprised.

> *"Communicating effectively is easy to do once you have a good teaching method and the right attitude. "*

Communicating effectively

The four keystones for effective communication in tai chi teaching are interrelated and positively reinforce each other. They are:

1.   Listening to your students.
2.   Making yourself understood.
3.   Using your 'emotional intelligence'.
4.   Applying tai chi principles.

Communicating effectively is easy to do once you have a good teaching method and the right attitude. They are all incorporated into my teaching method, the *Stepwise Progressive Teaching Method*, in Chapter 5.

Listening to your students

Stephen Covey in his book *The Seven Habits of Highly Effective People*[8] says: 'Seek first to understand, then to be understood.' That is, to communicate with your students, you must first listen to them.

Most people think of themselves as better listeners than they really are, so make sure you listen carefully. A good way to find out if you have truly been listening is to repeat in your mind what someone just said to you — you might surprise yourself with what you thought was said to you! Another good self-check of your listening skills is to ask yourself the following questions: Do I ever finish off a sentence for someone I'm listening to? Do I interrupt people before they finish a sentence? Are there occasions when I feel I can't wait for the person to finish talking and I jump in with a quick answer the minute they have finished? If your answer to any of these questions is yes, then the chances are you are not as good a listener as you think you are.

> *"Most people think of themselves as better listeners than they really are..."*

In tai chi we communicate not just by words, we also communicate with our mind, body and feelings. To communicate effectively you must 'listen' with your ears, eyes and mind to your students. Knowing your students' objectives, learning styles, relevant medical conditions and feelings will improve your teaching. Simply teaching the same package to everyone is like a doctor giving the same treatment to all his patients, regardless of their individual medical conditions. It may work for some, but could be inappropriate or even dangerous for others.

Jack is a caring teacher who always tries hard to help his students. One day he was asked a question, but being anxious to help and not to hold up the rest of the class, he did not listen carefully and rushed in with a detailed answer. Unfortunately he did not answer the right question. The student tried again to explain the question and Jack become more anxious as the rest of the class was getting restless. So he rushed in again, giving what proved to be another wrong answer. While this went on the rest of the class either wandered off or talked among themselves. If he had listened carefully, he could have answered the question correctly in much less time.

Getting to know your students can be done in many ways, depending on circumstances. Chaz calls his students a few days before their first lesson to welcome them. He tells them what to wear, what to expect and asks if there is anything he can do to make their first lesson more productive. Little wonder his students adore him!

Many teachers get their students to fill in a form beforehand, with their objectives, medical conditions and other important information (you'll find a sample enrolment form in the Appendix). If you use them, you should carefully read these forms before the first class.

You may have your own favourite method of getting to know your students before you meet them. The most important thing is to 'listen' in a receptive frame of mind at all times. Remember in tai chi, we communicate with our mind and feelings as well as our body. If you close your mind to them, your students will soon know.

> *"Remember that you can communicate with body and feelings as well as words."*

At the first face-to-face meeting, try to establish a connection with each student. A first impression can last a long time and a good start makes the rest of the journey so much easier. Greeting your students with a smile and, if appropriate to their culture, by shaking hands with them, is an excellent way to get connected to people. Your attitude is often well communicated at the first meeting. A good way to connect is to introduce yourself and ask your students to introduce themselves in turn and tell you and the other students what they want to achieve from your lessons.

Spending time to establish a connection with your students is a highly effective use of your time. As an example, in the case of doctor and patient relationships in USA, studies have shown that doctors who spend time establishing a connection with their patients have a better relationship with them, which leads to better therapeutic results — and they are also significantly less likely to be sued by their patients! Studies have shown that the time needed to establish a good connection between doctors and their patients is just three minutes.

A good doctor–patient relationship makes the rest of the doctor's work easier and more effective. For tai chi teachers, a different type of relationship is required. For a first meeting, often a smile and the right attitude can be sufficient for a good connection. After you have made a connection with your students, you can communicate with them better.

A common mistake many teachers make is their anxiety to establish their credentials at the first meeting. I often hear teachers go on for a long time about the well-renowned teachers they've studied with, how well qualified they are and what a high level of tai chi they've achieved. The truth is, like Mary Kay said, 'People don't care how much you know until they know how much you care.' People are only interested in what you can do that will benefit them, so confine your self-introduction to what qualifies you to deliver these benefits.

The method of communication varies with the size of the class. When working with a group, it is important to be aware of each person individually and also the group dynamic. If you spend all your time with the most vocal student and ignore the quiet majority, it will be ineffective and unfair to them. I often see novice teachers who spend most of their time focusing on the most vocal student, or helping the worst student. This approach will end up displeasing the whole group, including the one who gets most of the teacher's time. The group is unhappy because they have been ignored and the worst student will probably be overwhelmed by too much attention. In Part 2 of this book, I will give you guidelines to working with a group.

Professor Vince McCullough of Saddleback College, California, USA, a respected professor of physical education and teacher of tai chi and yoga for more than 40 years, says this about me: 'Dr Lam possesses the most important quality for master teaching: he first listens with his eyes, mind and heart; then he instructs. Most teachers just teach to a preconceived plan and miss the nuances and needs of their students.' It requires hard work and much training to learn how to listen, but it is the most rewarding thing I have learned. If I can train myself to listen well, there is no reason why you cannot.

Making yourself understood

The next keystone to communicating effectively is to make yourself understood. Remember that you can communicate with body and feelings as well as words. Tai chi is an art that involves 'doing'; a lot of talking and no 'doing' will not work. Lui is an experienced teacher from China who speaks little English, but she is able to teach quite effectively. In fact, she is much more effective than Kay's teacher, who overwhelms new students with too much information.

Naturally, being able to speak the same language is a significant advantage. Take full advantage of this by making your instructions and information clear, simple and relevant. Watch your students, and if they look puzzled, simplify your instructions. Give them one task at a time. Imagine if you were to give an instruction like this to a group of beginners for the Yang-style *Brush Knee* movement: 'Bend your knees so that your knee cap is in the same vertical line as your toes; turn 45 degrees to your left; step to the left with your left foot two feet from your right foot and at a 90 degree angle, with your heel touching down first; don't stand up; keep your body at the same height; with your left toes pointing at 90 degrees to the left...' and so on. It would be overwhelming and confusing for your students.

It is more effective splitting movements into small parts and teaching them one small step at a time. Students will often copy their teacher's movement, so there is no need for you to voice every little detail of each movement. Adjust your communication according to your students' progress. I will provide sample instructions on how to do this in the *Stepwise Progressive Teaching Method* in Chapter 5.

It is the teacher's job to create a friendly interactive environment, so that everyone feels comfortable and receptive to you. At the same time, maintaining good control of your class is important so that all your students can learn. Jack is a friendly and very caring teacher and he answers all questions in detail. Often when he spends a long time answering a question from one student that is irrelevant to the others, the rest of the class become restless and wander off to do their own thing. This is an example of good intentions leading to ineffective communication. Manage your class so that the entire group can hear and learn from you. Making yourself understood applies to the entire class.

A teacher can achieve good control of their class and at the same time be friendly and interactive. The secret is to be polite, firm and clear about your objectives. Encourage good questions, defer and discourage bad questions. Here is how.

Good questions are the best feedback you can get. They tell teachers what their students are interested in and how well they are learning. Encourage such questions with words and body language. Tell the questioner it is a useful question, smile or nod to

> *"A teacher can achieve good control of their class and at the same time be friendly and interactive."*

acknowledge it and then give a relevant but concise answer. A good question is usually one that is relevant and useful to the whole class, so ensure the class understands the question and make the answer interesting to them all.

Have you noticed there are usually just a few students in each of your classes who ask all the questions? Some students never stop asking questions! If you manage the situation badly, you can offend the questioner and, at the same time, deprive the rest of the group of their learning time.

Try to find out why some people ask so many questions — finding the cause of any problem is necessary before finding the solution. There are usually a few students who ask many irrelevant questions. People often ask me about part 2 of a movement while I am teaching part 1. Some students may feel insecure about their learning ability and they ask the question about part 2 to distract me so that I won't notice how bad (they think) they are at learning part 1! They often do this without being conscious of doing it — it is a psychological self-defence mechanism. Yet again, there are other people who ask very complex questions in order to be recognised for their knowledge of tai chi. Do you remember some students you've had, who keep distracting you with questions? Maybe they belong to one of these types.

If you understand what motivates these types of questions you can work out ways to deal with them. Listen to and acknowledge all questions, but don't necessarily answer them straight away. If it's a good question that is relevant and useful for the whole class, let the class know that they can benefit from listening to the answer before you start giving your answer. If the question is not relevant to what you're teaching the class at that moment, offer to answer it later or to talk to the person after class. Be polite and firm and if you offer to come back to it later, be sure you do that. If you think that person needs recognition, then provide appropriate recognition. One day in a Tai Chi for Health workshop, an experienced practitioner asked me a complex martial art application type of question. I complimented his depth of knowledge and asked him if he wouldn't mind discussing it with me after the class, as the focus of the workshop was on health.

When I'm very pressed for time, I ask students to hold their questions until I get through to a certain point. Often when I get to that point I find that, because my teaching system has been so effective, my students have learnt it all well and there is now nothing left for them to ask. Another method I use, when appropriate, is to use the question as a lead in to what I was planning to do anyway. For example, someone may have asked me how fast they should do one movement, so I get the class to practise with me at the right speed doing the movement we had just learned. I was intending to get the class to practise that anyway. By getting the whole class involved in practice, you have also stopped other questions. This tactic works especially well when there are too many questions and you are losing control of your lesson plan.

When students start to look inattentive or if you are being interrupted by too many questions, bring your students' attention back to the lesson by getting them to practise something together. As they practise, they learn. Remember tai chi is an art involving doing: by repeatedly practising, we learn. Often after practising a new move several times, students will find the answer to their questions anyway, just from doing it.

When you demonstrate a movement yourself with your body and heart, it is a powerfully effective form of communication. Your students will learn much from just following your movements.

Earlier in this chapter, I gave an example of a good teacher who took another teacher's class and got better results than the other teacher, despite it being a new and supposedly 'boring' topic. Other studies have also found that most effective teachers share similar attributes. These include having a good understanding of the topic (in our example, the good teacher was able to quickly develop an understanding of the new topic), making the material relevant to their students and involving their students in the learning process (this also stimulates them to think). Good teachers don't expect their students to remember things they can't remember themselves, nor to understand concepts that they themselves do not understand. So, 'making yourself understood' includes understanding the topic and also making the material relevant for your students.

> *"Good teachers don't expect their students to remember things they can't remember themselves, nor to understand concepts that they themselves do not understand."*

Using your 'emotional intelligence'

One day I was teaching a very talented student, Jackie, which usually is a most pleasant experience. Jackie picks up everything quickly, practises diligently and progresses really quickly. At one point, I tried to show her how to express internal energy as she turned her hand in a Yang-style *Cloud Hand*. It is not an easy thing for others to grasp, but for Jackie it should have been easy. For some reason, that day she didn't get it. I showed her a couple more times and said to her that it was unusual that she did not get this, since she had grasped more difficult concepts quickly before. From that point on, she got even worse. I began to feel frustrated. Recognising my own irritation, without noticing the closed look in her face, I stepped back mentally from the situation and let her work by herself. I put myself into a state of mental quietness (jing), and soon my mind became clear and I started to notice the closed look in her face. Then I realised that something that I had just said had put her into her 'personal shell'. Her mind was, as a result, partially shut down and she was not in her normal, effective learning mood.

This can happen to any learner. If you are not aware of it and keep trying to push your way through a closed mind, it can end up being a negative experience for both learner and teacher. It can also happen in real life outside teaching — understanding your own 'emotional intelligence' and that of the person you are interacting with can improve communication dramatically and help you avoid serious negative outcomes. For teaching it is important that you understand both your own and your students' 'emotional intelligence'.

Daniel Goleman explained the concept of 'emotional intelligence' in his book *Working with Emotional Intelligence*[9]: 'Emotional intelligence' refers to the capacity for recognising our own feelings and those of others… and for managing emotions well in ourselves and in our relationships.' Recognising your own feelings and the feelings of your students is critically important for effective communication. When people are pushed into their 'personal shell', their mind closes, their body becomes stiff and they are not in an effective mood to communicate or learn. Trying too hard to penetrate that shell can result in hurting the person and the relationship.

> *"Recognising your own feelings and the feelings of your students is critically important for effective communication."*

For the purpose of this book, I will briefly describe how the concept of 'emotional intelligence' relates to teaching and learning. I recommend you read Daniel Goleman's book *Emotional Intelligence*[10] and its sequel *Working with Emotional Intelligence*[9] for a thorough understanding of this topic. These books are extremely well written and useful for anyone.

The very incident that stimulated me to write this book happened five years ago when I was helping two instructors with a class. There was one student, Lisa, who was having problems with a certain move. The main instructor, with the best intention of being helpful, asked the assistant instructor to take Lisa aside to help her catch up. Suddenly Lisa rushed out of the room in tears. I followed her, sat with her, and talked to her for a very long time. I found out that Lisa had serious personal problems and she had come to the tai chi class looking for relaxation and ways to help her deal with her personal problems. When the teacher singled her out for a special catch-up lesson, Lisa saw this as a form of punishment for her slowness in learning. Lisa retreated into her 'personal shell' and reacted strongly by running away in tears.

I have often witnessed incidents similar to this when for some reason students have retreated into their 'personal shells', and both teacher and student have had a negative experience. It is difficult to repair the damage done to both parties and their relationships when this happens; it is much easier to avoid these incidents. Understanding these concepts can help you minimise the chance of them happening.

Understanding the concept of 'personal shell'

What is a 'personal shell'? I have created this term to help describe what happens when someone withdraws behind an invisible wall around themselves. Inside this wall, the person feels safe, as they did in their mother's womb; there is no communication with the outside world. Experiences like this can be very distressing to them and their teacher. Sometimes the person may feel threatened and hit out either physically or emotionally to hurt the person who put them there, despite the fact that they know that this person had good intentions. Inside their personal shell, the person hits out without consideration because they are reverting to the primitive reaction when their survival is under threat.

Practically everyone has a personal shell they can withdraw into for 'safety' when threatened. Two things often put people there:

1. Subconscious perceptions

As we grow up from infancy, our experiences impact on us like new writing on a piece of clean white paper. Those early experiences are strong and last for ever. As we grow older, other experiences appear as new writing on the paper and over-write the original experience. However, the original experience, which might not by now be a conscious memory (that is, not visible on the paper), still exerts a strong influence on our behaviour in a subconscious way. Have you ever tried to be calm on an important occasion and found you just cannot control your own emotions? This is the subconscious you exerting a stronger control over the conscious you.

Going back to our experiences in infancy, we were then totally dependent on our parents or carers. They were much bigger than us and when they spoke it sounded like thunder — they were like we'd imagine gods to be. As a baby, your entire existence and well-being depends on your parents and they solve all your problems for you. As a result, we grow up with a strong and deep imprint that we are incompetent and need help. No matter how careful our parents were when bringing us up, we have an almost natural lack of self-confidence and self-esteem within our subconscious mind. Better parents will have more secure children, but because of the way we've grown up, everyone has a certain degree of insecurity. If you're interested in reading more about this topic, Thomas Harris, in his book, *I'm OK, you're OK,* explains this concept extremely well[11].

Insecurity, when it becomes unbearable, puts people into their personal shell where they don't communicate or think rationally. The shells are insulated from the outside world and feel totally 'safe', as if you had a security door you could close, or, like the ostrich, you could bury your head in the sand. In infancy or childhood, this tactic gives us sanity and security. If you have children of your own, do you remember sometimes when they got upset by very minor things and ran into their room and shut themselves off from you? My friend Deborah was so worried that her daughter might do something to hurt herself, when she locked herself in her room after a heated argument, that she broke the lock open — and was very surprised to find her daughter browsing her bookshelves as though nothing had happened! Then Deborah realised that her daughter needed her own personal space when she thought she was being threatened. This mechanism may work for a child, but it is not an effective coping mechanism for adults, especially when they are trying to learn something new and they are not really threatened.

Insecurity is not all bad; it encourages us to be more careful, to work harder to achieve our goals, and drives us to save up for rainy days. When insecurity is so overwhelming that it becomes a disabling force against rational thought, then it becomes a hindrance to effective learning and many other coping strategies.

2. A perceived physical or mental threat

The primitive part of our brain has the capacity to short-circuit the newer logical thinking part (the neocortex). A perceived physical or mental threat can put us instantly into our personal shell, without the benefit of the thinking brain checking whether it is a real threat. This was a useful mechanism in ancient times when we were surrounded by predators and a hostile environment; we needed to be able to react quickly without thinking it through, so that we could survive a sudden attack. An example of this is when a sudden loud scream or noise can quickly make you jump. The reaction to jump is the 'fright and flight' reflex caused by a perceived threat. The noise may of course be just your children screaming at the television! Once your thinking brain has had time to think and analyse the situation you will calm down. At the moment you jump, all your body's resources are channelled into the muscles, so that you can fight or run away quickly. Very effective when needed to save us from attack by a lion, but a waste of energy when it's caused by your children's reaction to something on television!

> *"…even minor incidents, like being singled out for some reason, can put us into our personal shell."*

A similar process occurs when we think we are under emotional threat — even minor incidents, like being singled out for some reason, can put us into our personal shell. Once we are in our personal shell we can either be distressed and withdrawn or we may hit out aggressively. Withdrawing into a shell or hitting out without thinking is not an effective coping mechanism. Very often the perceived threat is not a real threat: after the logical thinking part of the brain has a chance to analyse the situation, a more effective solution will be found, as happened in the cases of Jackie and Lisa.

The main point to remember is that this mechanism is controlled by the subconscious and primitive part of the brain. In a threatening situation, the logical thinking brain does not function well. Even though it was plain to everyone else but Jackie or Lisa that they were not really threatened, the primitive part of their brain had perceived it so and disabled the thinking brain, causing them to withdraw into their shells. Once inside their shell their logical thinking power is shut off. If a teacher recognises when this is happening and allows time and space for the students, they may come back out of their shells. Better still, a teacher who understands the mechanism can avoid putting people there in the first place.

Once you learn to recognise the signs of someone retreating into their personal shell, you can use tai chi methods to help put yourself into a mental quietness or jing state. In the case of Jackie, I realised my own irritation and stepped back, which then allowed me to recognise the situation and give her time to regain her composure and come out of her personal shell. But if I had not put myself into the jing state, I would not have seen the closed look on her face. If I'd kept trying to push through the same point, it would have resulted in her ending the lesson feeling incompetent. If she encountered many of these experiences it would dampen her interest in learning and possibly even in tai chi altogether.

> *"Better still, a teacher who understands the mechanism can avoid putting people there in the first place."*

'Jing' is a mental state you can achieve through practising tai chi. Your level of jing correlates with your level of tai chi skill. (For more information on how to improve jing and tai chi see Chapter 11 and my book, co-authored with Nancy Kaye, *Tai Chi for Beginners and the 24 Forms*[12]). In the jing state, our minds are focused on our posture, body awareness, breathing, loosening our joints, relaxing and mental serenity. When practising tai chi, you strive towards that mental quietness and so, no matter what level of tai chi you have attained, you will have reached a certain level of mental quietness. At any time of crisis, you can step back mentally and put yourself in that state. In the state of mental quietness you can see the situation better and deal with it more rationally.

Keith is a highly skilled martial artist who also teaches tai chi. He always has problems controlling his temper. Sometimes Keith views a question from one of his students as a challenge to his authority. His reaction to such a challenge is to give an aggressive demonstration on the student who asked the question. In doing this, he sometimes hurts the student, so students become too scared to ask questions. It should come as no surprise to find that Keith has only a handful of students. Keith and others like him would benefit from learning how to use jing. By integrating the essential principles into their tai chi practice and daily life they will become better teachers as well as improving their tai chi.

The best approach is for a teacher to prevent their students from withdrawing into their personal shells in the first place. Useful methods include being positive and avoiding giving criticism, especially not singling out one person in front of others for any reason. Try to identify the students who are more sensitive and pay particular attention that you do not to put them in a position where they could feel incompetent or threatened.

One of the early signs is when a student becomes defensive. I used to get irritated when I suggested a point of improvement to a student and that student started showering me with excuses why they did not already know that point. I used to tell myself that they would learn more if they didn't waste their time giving me excuses and just listened and absorbed what I was teaching them. Now I understand that students who do this are feeling uncomfortable and could be close to retreating into their personal shell, I don't get irritated any more, but just back off gently. This allows the student time to relax, think it through and continue learning. It is a good policy to adopt Heather's approach and simply not single out anyone for correction. Until you get to know your students better, it is safer than risking putting people into their shells. Have you noticed how some people will shower you with excuses when you are trying to help them improve something they do, not just in tai chi but also in your daily life? Recognise it and back off so that the person does not retreat into their personal shell.

Applying tai chi principles

Tai chi was created based on nature. Sun Lu-tang (1861–1932), one of the greatest tai chi masters in history and creator of the Sun style, said that the highest level of tai chi is understanding the Dao. The Dao is based on the ancient Chinese philosophical understanding of the universe, often referred to as the way of nature. The ultimate goal of tai chi is to achieve harmony with nature. In nature, we have both yin and yang, with motion and stillness complementing each other, for example, calm and stormy weather. These principles can be applied to improve your teaching of tai chi.

Let us look at some of tai chi's essential principles and how they can be applied to teaching. Tai chi movements are well controlled so that they are slow, even (same speed) and continuous. Tai chi has a rhythm that is unrushed and flows smoothly. Applying this principle to teaching means that you should not rush your students, nor shower them with too much information or techniques before they and you are ready. Take time to teach everything smoothly and carefully, while maintaining the flow.

"The ultimate goal of tai chi is to achieve harmony with nature."

The mind controls the body and is aware of its movements. Effective teaching includes thinking about and being aware of what you do and say. Are your words meaningful to your students? Are they understandable at their level and are they relevant to them? Also, are the exercises and practices you teach meaningful, understandable and relevant to your students? Teaching something too complex for your students will overwhelm them and saying irrelevant things can cause them to disconnect from you.

When you do a tai chi movement, there is always a preparatory phase, after which you do the main part of the movement, ending up in a position ready to connect to the next movement. With teaching, there are the same three phases — preparing your lesson, teaching it and then preparing your students for their next lesson. In other words, there are three phases: preparation, execution and follow through. I will discuss this principle further in Chapter 6 when I tell you how to structure, prepare and coordinate your lessons.

We practise tai chi one step at one time, moving in a natural and steady rhythm. If you rush to do several movements in a hurry, it will not be good tai chi. Taking time to teach one step at a time is essential for effective teaching.

Earlier on in this chapter, I discussed the jing state and how useful it is for emotional intelligence. The jing state is also useful in allowing teachers to be aware of the big picture. Rather than focusing on one or two difficult students, be aware of the general feel of your entire class: it will make you a more effective teacher.

One of the core principles of tai chi is balance. Tai chi emphasises physical and mental balance. Good teaching should be well balanced, with the right amount of practice and theory, conducted at an even tempo and in a serene atmosphere. An irritable teacher who yells at a student who is trying to close a door to stop a draught is not as effective as a more mentally balanced teacher.

Working with nature, is like a willow tree that bends with the wind and bounces back. The willow tree is strong and elastic so that it can absorb the incoming force by moving with the wind so that it does not break easily. The soft absorbing nature is yin and the strength to bounce back is yang.

A useful practice drill for applying these principles to tai chi is *Push Hands*. In this drill, two partners start by putting their hand/s on the other's arm/s to feel each other's incoming force (this is usually termed 'listening to each other's force' in tai chi). In practising *Push Hands*, one person pushes and the other yields to the incoming force, like the willow tree yields to the wind. As they yield, they absorb the incoming force and at the same time 'listen' for the direction and strength of their partner's force, then redirect this force according to its direction and strength, adding their own force to gain control of the encounter.

Many people think that *Push Hands* is a contest, to push their partner away or 'uproot' them, so defeating their partner. They often push each other with brutal force. The ultimate aim of *Push Hands* is much more than this; it is to learn the skills that lead you to a harmonious relationship with your partner and with nature. In practising *Push Hands*, both partners learn the tai chi way of using energy with their partner. The skill of listening to the incoming force, yielding, adhering, neutralising, redirecting and delivering force are all based on learning about your partner's and your own energy. As your partner pushes, you yield, absorb and redirect; as your partner become receptive, you deliver energy. The interchange of energy flows like the tai chi symbol — continuous and complimentary. Both partners improve their qi (internal energy) from the practice and both become more skilful and stronger with the continual flow of energy. The ultimate aim is to harmonise with each other and with nature.

In teaching tai chi, the relationship is not that of master and slave, or winner and loser. It is an interactive relationship; there is an exchange and sharing of energy and knowledge that ultimately leads to harmony with each other, benefiting both teacher and student.

> *"The ultimate aim of* Push Hands *is to learn the skills that lead you to a harmonious relationship with your partner and with nature."*

To apply tai chi principles, start by listening to your students, understanding their objectives, their style of learning and their feelings. After absorbing this information, you can use this to find the most effective teaching method that will direct your students towards their goals. Think of listening and yielding to your student's incoming force as a way of getting to know your students. Working out the best way to teach is directing your force back to them. Through the interaction, you and your students learn about each other and grow into more skilful and stronger people. In real life, it means listening, being sensitive to your students' needs, sharing your knowledge in the way it is best absorbed, learning as you go, so at the end both you and your students are in harmony and have become healthier and stronger.

Jef Morris, an effective teacher, sent me this: 'Working with new students, who may become new teachers, each will make their own contribution in their time. Tai chi, like the universe, is not static and the continuation of teaching tai chi safely and effectively comes from the rising generations of students who may become great teachers.'

Facilitating enjoyment

For those of us who enthuse about tai chi, practising tai chi gives us a wonderful feeling in our body and mind. Tai chi intrinsically is an enjoyable exercise/art/sport. It is this enjoyment that urges us to practise and to share our enthusiasm with others. If people don't enjoy doing something, they will soon stop doing it.

To an outsider, tai chi looks graceful, effortless and enjoyable. Often people like the look of tai chi so much and imagine they could do it easily. In reality, beginners have to go through an awkward or even clumsy stage before they can attain that grace and enjoyment. Without knowing what to expect, the initial clumsy stage can put people off; they may think they will never reach the enjoyable stage.

I remember in my youth, I was fascinated with the beautiful music that came from the violin and I begged my father to let me learn it. The violin is a delicate instrument and quite difficult to learn. The sound a beginner produces is awful — the Chinese often describe the sound of someone learning the violin as 'killing the chicken'! I don't remember how many thousands of chicken-killing sounds I produced, but the learning process made me feel quite incompetent. Many tai chi beginners feel the same about learning tai chi, and they often give up for this reason. I can assure you that learning tai chi is definitely easier than learning to play the violin, especially if you are taught through my teaching method.

Help your students to find the intrinsic enjoyment of tai chi. Guide them through the initial awkward phase, the plateau phases and the rough patches and inspire them to practise regularly and to enjoy tai chi and its benefits. If you can do this, you'll have attained the greatest level of success a teacher can achieve. Here are a few more ideas to help.

Tell students what to expect and help them to feel competent

I find it helpful to tell beginners what to expect. I tell them that tai chi is very different from the Western sports and lifestyle they are used to. Most Western sports emphasise fast and strong movement in a straight line. In our modern world, we often move too fast and are always looking for short cuts to make it quicker. With tai chi, we move slowly, and in a curve instead of a straight line, because these ways bring us back to harmony with nature and our body. I tell beginners that tai chi is so different it will take them time to get used to it. I ask them to allow themselves and their teachers time so that they can get used to tai chi. I tell them that most people will become comfortable with it in three months and stress the enjoyment and health benefits they will get out of it if they persevere. I want them to understand, without actually saying it, that if they do not achieve what they expect, in the time they want to, it is not their fault — it is the nature of the art. I also help them to appreciate and cherish any progression they have made.

Sometimes they don't see the benefits of exercise immediately, so if the teacher can help them understand how tai chi works to improve their health and why it takes some time to produce results, this could help them to stay in the class. It is our experience that most people will stick with tai chi if they keep coming to classes for around three months or more. Many studies have shown the health benefits of tai chi after just three months of practice, which should provide more incentive for the students to stay. When they know what to expect, they are less likely to feel incompetent and give up. Give them a goal and a time frame to help them to persevere with tai chi.

Many years ago my patient Bob, an A-grade cricket player in his younger days, started tai chi to improve his health. Bob told me that he had lasted only three weeks because he felt so clumsy and incompetent that he gave it up. If Bob's teacher had told him what to expect, he might have stayed and got to enjoy tai chi.

Sometimes if a student feels their class is too difficult they can get discouraged and give up. It helps for the teacher to know more about what the student is looking for and to involve the student in their learning process.

Make learners feel good about themselves

People feel good about themselves when they learn to do something well. Professor Albert Bandura, of Stanford University, in his self-efficacy model of learning, emphasises the importance of being able to master a skill, because it positively reinforces the learner's perception of their own efficacy (effectiveness) and improves their ability to learn more. He says in his book, *Self-efficacy: The exercise of control*[13]: 'Enactive mastery experiences are the most influential source of efficacy information because they provide the most authentic evidence of whether one can master whatever it takes to succeed.' An effective teacher helps learners to master a skill by making it reachable and easier to learn.

Each individual tai chi movement has many requirements, such as controlling the speed of movements, coordinating the body, loosening the shoulder and sinking the elbow. Many novice teachers are eager to share their knowledge with students and so they shower them with all these requirements right at the beginning. It is not possible to acquire all these skills in one go. The intention is good, but not the result.

One of my patients, Jose, a meticulous accountant, went to a beginner's class. Jose told me that it was difficult to remember the sequence of the movements as well as the requirements, like sinking the elbow, loosening the shoulder and maintaining balance. Being a meticulous person, Jose wanted to do them all. By trying to do all these things, he became quite confused and could not manage to remember even the sequence of the movements. As a result, he felt incompetent. It is especially important for people to remember the sequence so that they can practise by themselves, not just during classes.

> *"People feel good about themselves when they learn to do something well."*

I have met many people who have given up tai chi and told me that tai chi is just not for them. For many, it was often the feeling of incompetence during the beginning phase that put them off. No one likes doing things they think they are not good at. In the case of Jose, I was able to talk to his teacher about it. She modified her teaching to focus on the basic shapes of the movements and place less emphasis on other requirements; increasing the practice time in the class and asking her students to work on just remembering the sequence of the movements. The teacher also referred her students to an article of mine, co-authored with Dr Yanchy Lacska, about using imagery to help remember tai chi. This is reproduced in full in Chapter 12. Jose felt much better and gradually got to enjoy tai chi. My teaching system is especially effective at helping students to become more self-efficacious (effective) learners.

Enhancing flow

Understanding the concept of 'flow' and how to achieve it will improve your teaching method from a different angle. Flow occurs when a person is so absorbed or so fully engaged in an activity that they 'lose all sense of time'. For example, it often happens when an athlete performs a new personal best, or an artist paints a masterpiece. Athletes sometimes call it 'being in the zone'. Whether it's a job, hobby, sport, or tai chi, when you are fully engaged you are likely to be in flow.

After years of studying many thousands of people, Professor Mihaly Csikszentmihalyi, the author of *Finding flow, the psychology of engagement with everyday life*[14] and the professor of psychology and education at the University of Chicago, has found a close correlation between enjoyment and the flow state. People whose lives are fulfilled and serene are more often in flow. He also found that it is possible to increase the time spent in flow. Professor Csikszentmihalyi says: 'When the heart, mind and will are at the same page, you are in a flow... In such a moment, consciousness is full of experiences and those experiences are in harmony with each other. In moments such as this, what we feel, what we wish and what we think are in harmony.' Being 'in flow' is similar to tai chi's state of body and mind being fully integrated.

> "People whose lives are fulfilled and serene are more often in flow."

Many years ago I built a large birdcage for our birds. I spent one day totally absorbed in planning and building this cage. I was not aware of how the time passed and it felt so good: I was in flow. I am not a good carpenter and the birdcage certainly wasn't a showpiece, but the experience was so enjoyable, I have since then kept finding similar projects to do. When I see tai chi teachers and students in flow as they teach and practise, they often tell me they enjoy tai chi very much. By helping your students to be in flow more often you will enhance their enjoyment of tai chi, improve their skills and greatly increase their chances of persevering with it.

There are three important factors that facilitate flow. Work to maximise these factors and you can have more flow. In tai chi, we aim to integrate the body and mind, which will take you to a mental state similar to flow. As your tai chi improves, you'll be in flow more often. More flow will bring you more enjoyment; more enjoyment will drive you to practise more and the more you practise, the more you will be in flow, thus setting up a positive cycle. The three factors are:

1. Having a clear goal or goals.
2. Getting immediate and relevant feedback.
3. Making sure your challenges and skills are well balanced.

Goal, in this case, means a short-term goal. For example, for a beginner the goal could be remembering the sequence of movements. You know right away if you remember your sequence correctly, so feedback is immediate and relevant. As far as balancing challenges and skill, an example might be that if you're a newcomer to tai chi and unfamiliar with the moves, trying to do them smoothly could be too much of a challenge for your level of skill. However, if you're an old hand at tai chi, you may already be doing your moves smoothly, so you'd now have no challenge at all. If the skill level required to do certain things is too easy and not enough of a challenge, then you become bored and are unlikely to be able to experience flow. If the skill required is too challenging for your level of skill, you become too stressed and flow is unlikely to come.

To enhance flow for your students, work on these three factors. Make their goals clear by teaching one small part at one time. Students need to understand what is required of them at their level in order to give themselves feedback. Empower your students to do this by keeping your instructions simple and easy to understand for the learner's stage of learning. For example, ask your beginners to centre themselves and step to the right, but don't emphasise any other requirements such as the precise direction and speed. Watch your students to ensure that their challenges and skill levels are well balanced. If a good number of the students can't do the movement, then adjust the goal to an easier level and make the requirements simpler. If the task is too easy, you can adjust the goal to a slightly more challenging level for them.

An excellent way to help your students feel the flow is to do more practice. Keep your students absorbed in practice with a specific goal, for example, focusing on even speed. When they begin to integrate body and mind, they'll enter flow. If you give them too much talk or complicated theory, it is less likely to induce flow.

Things that disturb flow from developing are:

- Giving too many points at once.
- Rushing through the lesson too fast.
- Criticising your students and putting them in their personal shells.
- Putting pressure on your students to perform to a set standard.
- Giving instructions that are not clear, not workable (try out your own instructions to see it they work), not relevant or not understandable.
- Having a fixed agenda (ie, a lesson plan that's not adjustable).
- Talking too much, especially on topics that students can't relate to.
- A chaotic class.
- Frequently interrupting when students are practising — avoid stopping students when they are showing you what they have learned.
- Students feeling intimidated, threatened or stressed.
- An uncomfortable learning environment (eg, too cold or too noisy).
- Students experiencing pain and discomfort — for example people with arthritis can be in pain if they have to stand in one position for a long time. (See Chapter 4: *Safety First.*)

Things that enhance flow development are:

- Being positive.
- Taking small steps.
- Clear instructions.
- Students being able to clearly see and hear the teacher.
- A friendly and encouraging environment.
- A calm and orderly class.
- A comfortable and tranquil atmosphere for learning.

- Being aware of your students' needs and abilities, and setting challenges in harmony with their skill levels.
- Leading by example: when you are in flow and enjoying the experience, your students will too.
- Enthusiasm.
- A sense of humour.

Encourage regular practice

Regular practice is a part of learning and enjoying tai chi. Encourage your students to practise regularly; start by setting a good example yourself. Help your students to enjoy practising and give appropriate positive feedback to those who have practised regularly. Offer students useful ideas to enhance regular practice, like setting up a daily routine and using my imagery method for memorising movements.

> *"An excellent way to help your students feel the flow is to do more practice."*

Give your students homework that is realistic and encourage them to set an individual goal that is attainable, such as the length of time they will practise each day. I will discuss this further in Chapter 6: *Organising your class*.

When it becomes appropriate, help them to understand the plateau phase and how to enjoy this phase. Help them to reach flow more often; to enjoy the rhythm of tai chi; the serenity; the pleasure of learning a new skill and of gaining better health.

Socialising and group dynamics

Many people come to tai chi for company and friendship and some come to classes to be with their friends. Socialising and interacting with a group is enjoyable — it is part of human nature. An effective teacher can do much to instigate and encourage social activities. Many students are motivated by these activities, which will help them to enjoy their tai chi more. In Chapter 6, in the section on 'follow through', I will discuss this further.

Chapter 3
How do you know that you are an effective teacher?

George Leonard, author of *Mastery*[1] says: 'To see the teacher clearly, look at the students. They are his work of art.' Your students are your indicator of how effective you are. Earlier in this book, Margaret gave this description of her teacher Bruce: '…[he] had some magic for me — and many others. It is hard to capture in words what someone has that makes 30+ people turn up twice a week, week after week.' Clearly Bruce's 30+ students are telling Bruce what an effective teacher he is.

"Your students are your indicator of how effective you are."

So are you an effective teacher? Have a look at your student retention rate; this will give you an indication of how effective you are. Most successful schools have a core group of students who stay with the school for years.

Have a good honest look at yourself. You are who you think you are, and if you believe that you are an effective teacher, there is a good chance you are. An effective teacher is receptive to feedback from students and is always proactively assessing the results, that is, how successfully their students have learned from them. Only with an open mind can you truly find out how effective you are.

An effective teacher is different from a 'great teacher' in the 'traditional' sense. According to Chinese tradition or belief, a highly skilled practitioner equals a great teacher. For example, according to legends, Yang Chan-fu's uncle, Yang Jian-hou was considered to be a great teacher because he had very high level tai chi skills. Yang Jian-hou, however, had a quick temper and had been known to break his students' arms in anger. Understandably, his style of tai chi never gained in popularity, probably due to its lack of students. On the other hand, Yang Chan-fu himself was good-natured and had many students. He has often been called the father of modern tai chi, as he was responsible for making Yang the most popular tai chi style. Clearly, Yang Chan-fu was a more effective teacher than his uncle.

I often wonder how true this legend is. I wonder if someone who was unable to control his anger really could have had such high level tai chi skills? But that is not relevant to the point I am putting forward here, which is that an effective teacher does not necessarily have to have high level tai chi skills.

Getting feedback about your teaching

Feedback from your students is important because it tells you how effective you are and provides direction on how you can improve your teaching skills.

If you encourage feedback, it will come to you in many ways. Feedback forms are one useful source. A good feedback form is simple, with questions that will give you useful answers and a space for open comments. There's a sample form in the Appendix, which will give you an idea of the types of questions you may ask. You can use this or adapt it to your own needs.

Phoning students who have stopped coming to your class is also a very useful method of getting good information about your teaching. The caller (yourself or another person) must be impartial, very polite and not put any pressure on the student to return. Use it as an opportunity to show that you care and offer them your assistance. If, for example, someone has told you they don't like your teaching style, offer a referral to another teacher with a different approach. Be very tactful and sensitive. Analyse their feedback with a receptive mind; you can gain very useful information from it.

The most useful feedback often comes informally through casual conversation, friendly discussion and body language. Arriving early or staying late after class is a good way to catch this sort of feedback without the pressure of being in class. Talk with your students and observe their reactions to your class; you'll learn a lot.

You can encourage good feedback by graciously accepting all feedback, even the most trivial and inappropriate. If a person gives you feedback and you start arguing about it with them, it will have the effect of stopping that person giving you any further feedback, good or bad. Likewise, if you keep giving excuses to someone who is trying to give you feedback, you will stop them giving more. Do you remember the last time someone was trying to give you some feedback, for instance to teach a little more slowly, and you started explaining why you did not do it that way? Maybe you tried to put the blame on someone else or a lack of time or something similar? You may have a very good reason why you are teaching faster than the student thought you should, but they are unlikely to be interested in this. Most people simply want their feedback to be acknowledged. Did you ever take any feedback as a personal attack and retreat into your 'personal shell' (see Chapter 2 for more about 'personal shell')? Or did you listen with your ears, eyes and mind, smile graciously and thank the person giving you feedback, with a promise to look into the matter? And did you look into the matter later and take what action you could?

> *"You can encourage good feedback by graciously accepting all feedback, even the most trivial and inappropriate."*

You can get feedback at unlikely times too. Do you remember occasions when soon after you had taught something, your students asked you a question about exactly what you had just taught? Does this leave you wondering if your students are sleeping through the lesson? If this happens, consider the possibility that you did not teach it effectively enough to be understood. If it happens frequently, then your teaching method needs to be seriously looked at. So don't get annoyed with your students if this happens; use this or similar occasions as a useful type of feedback.

An effective teacher who has good control of their 'emotional intelligence' (see Chapter 2 for more about 'emotional intelligence') can extract good feedback from any kind of interaction, even unpleasant ones, such as when a student who has little experience in tai chi and teaching tells you in a 'lecturing' tone of voice how to improve your tai chi teaching. If you can suppress the expected emotional reaction ('How dare you lecture me! What do you know about it?'), and analyse what this person is saying, to see if there is any substance in it, then you will be a master in collecting feedback.

Try answering these questions, using them as a checklist to find out how effective you are and which areas you can improve.

1. Do you enjoy making your students feel good about themselves?
2. Do you make your students feel good about their learning capabilities?
3. Do you know your students' objectives?
4. Do you have a plan of how to help your students get to these objectives?
5. Are you satisfied with your students' progress? If you are always unhappy with their progress consider the possibility that you are an ineffective teacher.
6. Do you look forward to your class?
7. Do you feel good after your class?
8. Do you have a high retention rate?
9. Do you have a core group of students who keep coming back?
10. Do your students feel comfortable about giving you feedback?
11. Do your students give you feedback? No feedback does not necessarily mean that you are a perfect teacher, it could also mean people sense that you are not receptive to it.
12. Do you check with health professionals how to teach safely?
13. Are you always looking for ways to improve your teaching skills?
14. Are you mostly positive in your teaching?
15. Do you teach in small enough steps for your students to understand?
16. Do you work well with different types of learners?
17. Do you communicate well with your students?

Analysing feedback

When you get feedback, it is important to analyse it carefully in a balanced way. It may not be easy to face negative feedback. Feedback is like a mirror — sometime we don't like what we see, so we tilt our face this way and that to give a different view. I remember early on in my teaching career, people said to me how remarkable it was that I could remember so many of my students' mistakes, and I took that as positive feedback on my teaching method!

To make best use of feedback, avoid fitting it into your own mind-set. Elaine, a dedicated teacher with good tai chi skills, has very high expectations of herself and her students. If any of her students don't perform to her standard, she often criticises them in front of the class. Elaine cannot accept negative feedback from dissatisfied students, so when she gets it, she re-frames it to fit her accepted mind-set. She sees such feedback as a result of her just happening to attract difficult learners. When she gets negative feedback from students she calls them troublemakers.

Not all feedback is appropriate or useful. In the same lesson, you could have one person saying that you are teaching it too fast and another too slowly. Analyse all feedback carefully with the aim of trying to find out what works best for the majority of the class and for you. You cannot please everyone, so don't try or you could end up pleasing nobody. My colleague Jef visualises letting the impossible demands slip down his back, like water off a duck's back. The key is to keep your students' objectives in mind — which method is more effective in helping most of your students achieve their goals?

It is important to gather your internal strength and mental balance before looking at feedback. Don't allow yourself to be disproportionally influenced by inappropriate negative feedback. Put things into perspective: is it the wish of your entire class or one very unusual student? And is it a realistic request? An example of an unrealistic request was when one of the participants in a workshop requested a very large practice area. To provide the requested space would have brought the cost of the workshop up to a prohibitive level, so, in this instance, clearly we had to let that feedback flow over us, like water off a duck's back. Again it goes back to whether you have achieved your aims. In that particular workshop, the vast majority of the students reported that they had more than fulfilled their objectives and even the person who requested the extra space can't have been too dissatisfied as he kept coming back to our workshops! There will be times when, despite negative feedback, you are sure that what you're doing is right; you just have to follow your heart.

> *"A confident teacher is open and receptive to feedback but does not let it demoralise them."*

Most importantly, use feedback to improve your teaching. No one is perfect, or knows everything about teaching. The key is to continue to improve. A confident teacher is open and receptive to feedback but does not let it demoralise them. Before implementing any suggestions, be sure to analyse them with the bigger picture and the end results you want to achieve in mind.

PART 2: THE SYSTEM

In Part 1 of this book, I talked about the benefits you can get from teaching tai chi, what skills you'll need to be an effective teacher and how you can find out if you are one.

In Part 2, I am going to tell you about a practical and easy-to-learn teaching system that I have developed over the last twenty years — the *Stepwise Progressive Teaching Method* — and give you a structure for your classes.

My system of progressive teaching has been used by thousands of tai chi teachers with great success. Professor Rhayun Song of Chungnam National University in Korea, a researcher and professional teacher, says this about my system: 'Tai chi is very easy to learn if you learn it step by step… We have never encountered anybody who cannot follow the progressive learning method.' Another recognised teacher, Professor Vince McCullough of Saddleback College, California, USA, a physical education, tai chi and yoga teacher for 40 years, says: 'In coaching there is a saying, "Practice doesn't make perfect; perfect practice makes perfect." The progressive teaching method is perfect practice.'

Before I tell you about the system and class structure, however, I have devoted a complete chapter to the topic of safety, because it is vitally important that you teach tai chi as safely as possible.

Chapter 4
Safety first

Introduction

When you are teaching tai chi, your students' safety is of paramount importance. Teaching safely makes you a more effective teacher. No matter what your students' objectives are, any injury will set them back from achieving them. It seems likely that if we don't take on this responsibility ourselves, governments might soon force us to do so. To safeguard the public, many countries are now bringing in regulations for the conduct of exercise classes. It may not have happened with tai chi classes yet in your country, but it could eventually. The benefit for us, if we take on this responsibility, is that we can probably do a better job than the government.

> *"No matter what your students' objectives are, any injury will set them back from achieving them."*

My colleagues and I have worked hard to make our Tai Chi for Health programs the safest possible and we teach the precautions outlined below in our workshops. To be certified to teach, participants must pass the test for safe teaching. The vast majority of tai chi instructors/leaders who have attended our workshops support this measure. Many told us that they wanted to learn about safety but couldn't find out where to learn it. Gary, a tai chi instructor for 10 years, had been suffering from back pain for the same length of time. He told me that after attending my workshop, he stopped doing the straight leg toe-touch exercise in his pre-tai chi warm up and his back pain has disappeared.

In 2005, Accident and Compensation Corporation (ACC), a government body in New Zealand, paid for 10,000 older adults to attend tai chi classes to improve their health and prevent injury. The ACC recognises the importance of safe tai chi teaching and invited me to help them design safety measures and set up training courses for class teachers, to be used throughout the country. I have used essentially the same guides as I do in my workshops. These are easy to learn and most of them are such common sense that you may be doing them already.

There are significant differences in different tai chi styles and schools, therefore the safety requirements for them are different. My guide here is based on commonly accepted variations of the 'soft' tai chi styles such as Yang and Sun. If you have any doubts about the forms you teach, I recommend you check with appropriate health professionals. All my Tai Chi for Health programs are designed in consultation with medical experts in their respective fields, with safety as the top priority. For example, the Tai Chi for Arthritis program has had input from arthritis specialists (rheumatologists and physiotherapists).

The notion that 'my teacher taught me this, so it must be safe' is just as faulty thinking as saying that my teacher knows everything there is to know about medicine now and into the future. There is a well-known saying in China that if you keep stamping on a stone (performing the Chen-style movement *Golden Guard Stamping on the Ground)* until you've bored a hole in the stone, you are then good enough to graduate from the Chen-style. I often wonder how many people have crushed their knee cartilages by 'stamping on a stone' like this! In fact I know of many Chen stylists who have suffered from serious problems with their knees.

Once you have the intention to minimise injury, you can find ways to do so. Start by using my guide here and make sure you constantly upgrade your knowledge. Remember, medical knowledge is updated constantly. You may have already been taking many of these precautions, but safety is so important that it is always worth revising your knowledge.

There are many medical conditions that are not obvious, even to a doctor's eyes. An exercise teacher is not a health professional, so be aware of your limitations. Dr Pam Kircher, a medical doctor from the USA, says that even though she is licensed to practise medicine, she never does so during a tai chi class. The reason why? Although she knows medicine and may be correct in the information she gives, she doesn't have the student's medical chart in front of her to review their history, lab tests, etc, so it's possible to miss something. For that reason, she doesn't feel it's right to give medical advice to students. She says, 'When I teach tai chi, I wear my tai chi hat, not my medical doctor hat.' Being a medical doctor too, I don't practice medicine in my tai chi classes; I refer students back to their health professionals. One day a student reminded me that I am his doctor, so I asked him to make an appointment to see me at the clinic where I have access to his medical records and our medical equipment.

When students enrol, consider asking them to complete and sign a medical waiver form for your protection. In that form there should be a statement to the effect that students acknowledge by signing the form that it is their own responsibility to tell you if there is any medical condition that may affect them doing tai chi.

It is also the student's responsibility, if they have any medical condition, to get their health professional's approval to take your class and for them to provide you with instructions about any special precautions that must be taken. I have provided a sample waiver form in the Appendix. Be sure to check with your legal adviser to ensure this form complies with your own country's legal requirements.

Safety precautions can be classified into four categories:

1. General care.
2. Exercise care.
3. Specific precautions for tai chi.
4. Precautions for people with special medical problems.

General care

Ensure a safe learning environment

Make sure your practice environment is safe. For example, make sure that it has good lighting, is clear of obstacles, has a non-slippery surface with no loose mats and is a comfortable temperature. I once visited a class in its practice hall. The teacher is also a painter and the hall had some of his paintings (some of which were framed with glass) spread out on the floor in one corner. Can you imagine what might have happened if one of his students had stepped on a painting and slipped on the glass?

Whether your class is being held inside a building or outside in the open air, make sure that the location has easy access. Avoid stairs and also places that are too cold, too hot or too windy.

If you are training for a long time, particularly when it is hot, your students may become dehydrated. Drinks should be provided, or ask your students to bring their own.

Prepare for emergencies

Have a written emergency procedure at hand that includes emergency phone numbers for students and the ambulance service's phone number. Ensure there is a telephone handy. In your emergency procedure, write down your venue's full address and details of how to

> *"Have a written emergency procedure at hand..."*

get there. Allocate different tasks to your assistants to do. For example, in the case of a student who collapses suddenly (which can happen anywhere), the teacher can tend to the student, assistant number one will call the ambulance and assistant number two will keep an eye on the other students and open the door for the ambulance service personnel.

In most Western countries, exercise leaders are required to have current first aid training. I believe tai chi teachers should do likewise. I also believe that it would be a good idea for all adults to have this training.

If any of your students has a medical condition which might affect them doing tai chi, find out from their health professional what precautions you should take.

Create a relaxed atmosphere

Create an atmosphere in which your students feel comfortable talking to you about their problems. Let your students understand that they should work well within their comfort zone. Stress to the students that they don't have to compete with anyone else or push themselves to achieve anyone else's standard.

I once saw a teacher pushing a student into a lower stance because they could not bend low enough — this is a very dangerous thing to do. When you are aware of your limitations and take care with your own movements, you are much less likely to incur injury than when you have an unpredictable outside force pushing you. What is more, a teacher who does this could be accused of causing injury or assaulting their student.

Get adequate insurance

For your own protection, you should have insurance that is valid in your country. In this day and age, teachers should be cautious about the possible legal consequences of their actions. Be careful not to touch anyone. If touching is unavoidable, ask your student for permission, and then do so very gently.

Exercise care

Avoid dangerous exercises

There are some dangerous exercises that are not part of most recognised 'soft' tai chi forms, although they could be part of your warm up exercises. Here are some of the common ones.

1. Flexing or bending your neck backwards. This causes over flexing of the spine, with the risk that vertebral discs may cause injury to the nerves in the neck.

2. Bending down with straight legs to touch your toes. This is a dangerous movement. It can over flex the spine and can cause injury to the discs or nerves of the back.

3. Bouncing when doing a stretch increases the chances of ligament damage.

4. Ballistic (sudden, vigorous or violent) movements can be dangerous, especially violent stretches of the lower back and hamstring muscles.

5. Doing a sit up with your hands behind your head can become dangerous when you use your hands and arms to pull yourself up. This can overflex your neck and may cause compression of inter-vertebral discs.

You can find more comprehensive technical information from sports medicine resources[1]. A good reference book, *Exercise Danger*[2], has a comprehensive list of these.

Take general exercise precautions

1.   Do not practise when you are very hungry, immediately after a full meal, or when you are very upset.
2.   Begin your session with warm-up exercises and end with cooling-down exercises. These help prevent injury, pain and stiffness. The length and extent of the warm-up depends on the intensity of the exercise program. My Tai Chi for Health programs include a set of warm-up exercises that you can use. These are included in Chapter 8.
3.   Avoid practising in a place that is too hot, too cold or is windy.
4.   Continue your session only for as long as you feel comfortable. Listen to your body and rest when you start feeling tired, are in pain, or lose concentration.
5.   Don't continue doing any movement that is painful or causes you discomfort. If you experience chest pain, shortness of breath or dizziness, or if additional pain in your joints persists, contact your doctor.
6.   Move well within your comfort range. The first time you do a movement, stretch to only 70 percent of your normal range of motion and increase that range gradually.

Specific precautions for tai chi

Many of the force-delivering movements in Chen-style tai chi have a higher risk of injury, so if you practise Chen-style, please take extra care and consult a health professional if you have any doubts.

Do all movements slowly and gently, as consistent with tai chi principles, avoid using excessive force, be focused and aware of your body's limits. If you follow the essential tai chi principles they will help you to minimise the risk of injury.

1.   Wear loose, comfortable clothing and well-fitting shoes.

2.   Gradually build up the length and number of practice sessions, aiming for about 20–40 minutes on most days (for older adults). A simple indication of how long to practise initially is the length of time you can walk comfortably at a steady pace. If you can practise for just 10 minutes in one session, you can do another 10 minutes after you have rested.

3.   Avoid moving a student's body and limbs to correct their position, if possible. If it is very important for you to do it, be sure to ask permission each time. If you move a student's body or limbs, you may aggravate an existing injury (which may not be obvious to you or the student), or be accused of causing one. Joseph is a teacher who frequently twists and moves his students' hands during his class. He thought that by asking the entire class once at his very first lesson, 'If anyone has an objection to being touched please come out and tell me', he would have no problem for all his subsequent lessons. However, most people don't like to say no in front of others and also they might not realise that an unexpected push could hurt them.

4.   If you are teaching classical Yang-style tai chi, some of the forms may involve turning the foot while the knee is bent with the weight on that foot. This can cause excess stress on the knee ligaments and can cause a twist injury to the knee. Consider amending the forms so that weight is shifted back before turning, to minimise the shearing force on the turns.

5.   Tai chi requires the knee to bend and stay at that bent level throughout a set of forms. This can cause too much stress to a person's joints. Make it clear to your students that while the goal of tai chi is to keep the knees bent, they should work up to that slowly. Encourage your students to stand up between movements, to avoid excessive stress to their knees. As their muscles become stronger, students will be able to stay comfortably and longer in a bent position.

6.   Tell your students that when they bend their knees, they should make sure their knees are directly above their toes, otherwise they may overstretch and injure the ligaments on either side of their knee.

7. When their knee is bent, looking from the side, their knee mustn't be pushed any further forward than the tip of their toes. Bending any deeper could cause too much strain to the ligaments.

8. Some movements involve a deep squatting position, with one knee touching the back of the other knee. This is a very stressful position for the knee joints, so you should modify this movement for your students to be well within their comfort zone. Be sure to warn any students who want to do the full range of the movement of the dangers involved.

9. Jumping can be dangerous, for example in the Sun-style *Double Patting Foot*. Make sure your students understand this, or, better still, modify the movement for them.

10. Advise your students to set up a regular time for practice, so their tai chi practice becomes a part of their daily routine. Regular practice keeps the muscles and ligaments well tuned, which helps to prevent injury.

11. Encourage students to talk to you about any movements they are finding difficult or uncomfortable.

12. Do all the movements slowly, continuously and smoothly. As students become more familiar with the movements, they will start to flow more easily and feel more graceful.

13. Breathe slowly, naturally and easily. As your students become more familiar with the movements, try to get them to coordinate their movements with their breathing, as instructed. If they find this feels uncomfortable, advise them to return to their natural breathing.

14. Advise your students to use the minimum effort necessary to do the movements and not to force any of them. This will help them cultivate qi and relax, and will also minimise injury.

15. Tell your students to follow your movements as accurately as possible within their comfort zone. If they find they can't do something comfortably, they should just do what is well within their comfort zone and visualise the full range of movement. For example, if the movement requires them to stretch out their elbow to 80 percent of the full range of motion, but they can

only stretch to 50 percent, then they should do the 50 percent and visualise that they are stretching to 80 percent. Gradually, they will be able to improve their stretch (studies have shown visualisation can improve range of motion).

Precautions for people with medical problems

There are several common precautions that should be taken by people with special medical problems such as arthritis or diabetes. Check with your student's health professionals to confirm what precautions are appropriate for that student.

Knee problems

Many people have arthritis in the knee joints. Tai Chi requires the knee to bend and stay at that bent level throughout the set of forms. Students with arthritis should stand up between movements to avoid excessive stress to their knees, until they develop strong muscles and ligaments.

"Check with your student's health professionals to confirm what precautions are appropriate for that student."

In classical Yang-style tai chi, many people turn their foot while their knee is bent and their weight is on their foot. People with arthritis should transfer their weight or straighten up before turning to avoid injury.

Hip replacement

People who have had a hip replacement operation should avoid crossing the foot on the affected side of their body over to the other side of their body. During the replacement operation, the nerves responsible for feeling in the opposite side of their body may be cut, so people who've had this operation may not be able to balance well if their foot crosses the midline of their body.

Standing qigong (zhan zhuang)

Doing standing qigong can have high risk of injury because standing on one spot puts extra stress on the body, especially the knee and hip joints. You can use a safer qigong like those described in my Tai Chi for Back Pain program. Older people and people with arthritis can injure their knees by standing for a long time in a stationary position.

Holding a position

If you want to correct a student's position do not hold them in the same position for long. Holding a position can be especially stressful for older people or people with arthritis and they have an increased chance of injury from doing this.

Shoulder problems

The shoulder is a very mobile joint that can be prone to injury. Many older people have arthritis and rotation cuff or other problems with their shoulders. Movements involving the shoulder should be done slowly, and moving the hands above the head should be done with care. Warn students to stop when there is any pain.

Hypoglycaemia

The most significant danger for people with diabetes is hypoglycaemia. 'Hypo' means low and 'glycaemia' means blood glucose (blood sugar). So hypoglycaemia is having low blood glucose. When a person's blood glucose gets too low, loss of consciousness and even brain damage can result. Hypoglycaemia affects diabetics who are being treated with medication or injections.

Exercise causes a high consumption of energy and therefore blood glucose can be depleted rapidly. The body has an efficient system to regulate blood glucose so that it stays in the right range. However, as medication or injectable insulin aims to lower blood glucose, they may interfere with the body's regulatory system and cause hypoglycaemia. This is why people with diabetes should let their doctor know what kind of exercise they are doing.

Most people with diabetes are well prepared by their health professionals to recognise signs and symptoms of hypoglycaemia. They are taught what to do. Most people with diabetes who are likely to get hypoglycaemia bring with them some food, drink or candies (such as jelly beans) just in case. Encourage them to feel comfortable with sitting down and eating whenever they feel the need. Some might bring a medication set with needle, syringe and testing kits. Don't be alarmed if they use it.

In case your students forget to bring their own, you might find it useful to bring with you a small package of jelly beans or a special package of glucose from a pharmacy, designed for averting a hypoglycaemic attack. Keep in mind that it requires four to six jelly beans to avert a hypoglycaemic attack. If you do bring a package, be sure it is well sealed and clean.

> *"It is important not to assume the role of a health professional in a class."*

Occasionally though, a student can lose consciousness too quickly, before you can take these preventative measures. Use your first aid training to position the student and call an ambulance (or if you've pre-arranged it with an assistant, get them to call while you attend to the student).

It is important not to assume the role of a health professional in a class. The teacher has responsibilities similar to those of an exercise leader and you should use your first aid training to do what is appropriate. However, beyond that, seek medical help.

Three fundamental rules for safety

Rule 1

Work with health professionals. Resist the temptation to play doctor. If you tell your student that their pain is minor and that they can continue to exercise, it could be considered that you've made a diagnosis and instituted medical treatment.

As a practising doctor, like Dr Pam Kircher, I seldom practice medicine in my teaching sessions, unless, of course, it is a medical emergency. If you are not a legally qualified health professional in your country, don't do anything you are not qualified to do.

Rule 2

Listen to your students carefully. Listen not only with your ears, but also with your eyes and your heart. If someone tells you they are not in pain but they look like they are in pain, they probably are. Advise that person to stop and consult their health professional; it is better to be safe than sorry. Remember to respect students' rights and just give the best advice possible as a tai chi teacher.

Rule 3

Encourage your students to listen to their bodies and to work within their comfort zone. Create a relaxed atmosphere in your classes so that your students feel comfortable about stopping and resting anytime they need to.

Chapter 5
The Stepwise Progressive Teaching Method

Introduction

Effective teaching is empowering for both student and teacher. An effective teacher empowers their students to learn, enjoy and develop themselves to their full potential through tai chi. My system, the *Stepwise Progressive Teaching Method*, makes learning easy for students, so that they feel good about their ability to learn. This enables them to learn more quickly and to enjoy learning tai chi more, which in turn will make you, their teacher, more fulfilled.

Mastering a skill is the most influential factor for making people feel good about themselves, as Professor Albert Bandura from the psychology department, Stanford University, USA, stresses in his self-efficacy model of learning. My system breaks down the complex art of tai chi into small easy to learn segments, which allows students to regularly experience the satisfaction of mastering a skill. Professor Bandura says this about breaking down complex skills: 'Development of the cognitive basis of human competencies is facilitated by breaking down complex skills into easily mastered subskills and organizing them hierarchically.'[1]

> *"An effective teacher empowers their students to learn, enjoy and develop themselves to their full potential through tai chi."*

A system will help you put all your skills into effective use. Like when you use a computer program — the process involves a series of logical steps you need to take to achieve your goal. When you have a system, everything falls into place. An effective system can make a complex art like teaching tai chi easy and enjoyable.

I have incorporated teaching skills, experience and tai chi principles into my unique teaching system. Over the last 20 years I have worked with many tai chi teachers and education experts to refine this system. I have used it with great success to teach thousands of students, from beginners to those competing in international competitions.

You may be surprised by the simplicity of my system. Often the most effective systems are the simplest ones. Take the time now to fully understand it so that later on you can remember how to adjust it for different situations.

The best way to appreciate any system's effectiveness is in its application in real life. Thousands of tai chi teachers have found out how useful my Stepwise system is.

Margaret Brade, a tai chi teacher and CEO of *Age Concern* from Stockport, UK says: 'I find the Stepwise process useful for students of all levels and abilities, and also for the teacher. For beginners it gives them a sense of achievement from learning the basic shape of the movement. For advanced students it gives an opportunity to learn more depth and refinement. For the teacher it ensures a steady pace and provides time to watch and give feedback to students, allows more teaching input and positive engagement with the students, leading to greater satisfaction all around. In addition it enables you to pick up on any health and safety issues — for example someone who has a limitation and may need to adjust the movement.'

I've received much feedback from learners that they have enjoyed learning through this method and found it very effective. Caroline Demoise, an experienced teacher from the USA, told me this: 'When I took over teaching at Southside Athletic Club in Bradenton, Florida, the students really appreciated my use of Dr Lam's Stepwise Progressive Teaching Method. These students had struggled to learn tai chi under their traditional teacher's guidance, which was expecting them to learn a whole movement after being shown it a couple of times. They were amazed at how I broke the movement down into small segments that they could grasp, how frequent repetition was used to reinforce the learning and how encouraging I was... This group has been with me for a year and a half and they continue to be surprised at how much they are able to learn and how much they enjoy it.'

Before you begin, if you have not already done so, please read Chapter 2 of this book to understand the theoretical basis of my system. The *Stepwise Progressive Teaching Method* is designed to work with different learners and situations, so it is a good idea to go back and re-read relevant parts of this book every now and then. Please note that the next chapter about class organisation is to be used hand in hand with this chapter.

I will briefly discuss a few fundamental points about effective teaching before I explain the details of my system. For more detail about these and other points read Chapter 2.

Be positive with your students

Giving positive feedback to your students is the single, most useful teaching technique you can learn. The feedback has to be meaningful and appropriate, so watch your students carefully, orientate yourself to look for good points, and then express your thoughts sincerely and appropriately. Just saying, 'This is good' is not as effective as saying 'This is good because your movement is very smooth'.

When you give feedback, use a 'positive sandwich'. Start with a positive point. 'Your movements are nice and smooth' and then give a point of improvement (optional), 'Try to slow down a little and see how you feel', then end it with a positive note, 'You have good body alignment'. Give one point of improvement at a time only, and never make a negative statement like, 'This is wrong, do it my way!'

Being positive also means having a positive attitude towards your students. Give them respect and expect a positive result from them. Speaking positively, for example, you would say 'Keep your body upright' instead of 'Don't lean forward'. Words like 'no' and 'don't' are negative; avoid them as much as possible. Being positive also applies to you. Be positive with yourself and believe in yourself.

Teach 'stepwise'

Teach 'stepwise', breaking down each movement into several small steps, teaching it step by step and in a logical progression and building it up slowly, as though you are going up a staircase.

One person will take one step at a time to get upstairs while another person may do three steps at a time, but in the end, both will get to the top. If getting to the top is your objective then that is all that really matters. In terms of learning tai chi, reaching the top in a hurry sometimes results in learning the outward shape only and missing out the essence of the art. The extraordinary thing about tai chi is that every small segment has many different layers within it, so that even a quick learner will have plenty to work on and will not be bored by taking one step at a time.

> *"Teach 'stepwise', breaking down each movement into several small steps, teaching it step by step and in a logical progression..."*

It is important to learn properly one step at a time because the human brain is programmed to learn better that way. It could appear to be a slow way of learning but in fact, in the end, it is the quickest way to learn tai chi.

Using the stepwise method, most students will be able to learn easily, and so will gain a sense of achievement. If you were to teach tai chi like Caroline's traditional teacher, who expects students to know a form after showing them a couple of times, most of your students would be frustrated and feel inadequate because they could not do it. And your more talented students, who learned it quickly, would miss out on the finer points. Students are more likely to be fulfilled and enjoy the exercise if they find they can do it well. After they have learned it, their confidence will improve and they will be able to continue to learn even more effectively.

I have often seen impatient learners get the basic shape of tai chi quickly by taking three steps at one time, while many slower learners just work steadily using a stepwise progression. A few years later, the slow learners will be way ahead of the fast learners because they have taken their time acquiring and digesting the essential tai chi principles.

Teach in a logical progression

Imagine you are building a house. You start with the foundations, then you build the ground floor, the walls and then the roof — everything is done progressively. If you were to mix all these tasks together and do them randomly, chances are the house would never be built. Learning by progression works best for most types of learners.

Cheryl Lee Player, a teacher of tai chi and dancing for 35 years from Newcastle, Australia, told her new students that learning tai chi is like painting: 'You start with sketching the shape of the picture, then fill in the colour and line, gradually adding the details in a step-by-step manner — eventually the complete beautiful picture will come up. You cannot skip steps and just get to the complete picture.' Not surprisingly, Cheryl is also an accomplished painter and illustrator (her illustrations for this book have added a wonderful artistic touch to it).

Define your starting point

Define your starting point and come back to it within each segment you are teaching. This is an anchor point to orientate students to the right direction, reduce confusion and facilitate learning. Clearly define your starting point at the beginning of each teaching segment.

Position yourself well

You need to be seen by the visual learners, be heard by the auditory learners and be in the right position so that people who cannot readily convert left to right can follow your movements. Position yourself with your back towards your students, so that it is easy for most of them to follow your movements. However, be sure to turn around and show your hand movements when they are not visible to your students.

In a class with many students, it may be necessary to move to different positions as you demonstrate, so that all of your students can see you. Some people teach facing their students, using mirror-image movements, but although it works well for many, there will be some students who are confused with this. Naturally when you teach a movement that is symmetrical, like *Open and Closing* Sun-style, it will be appropriate to demonstrate it while facing your students.

Adapt your teaching for different size groups

Adjust your teaching to the size of your class, based on your experience and on circumstances. As a general guide, the larger the group, the more you should prepare your class and the closer you should stick to my Stepwise teaching system. Clarity is especially important, because if you are unclear, you'll be asked questions, which will disturb the flow and slow down the learning process. If you're bombarded with questions you could even lose control of your class. Good preparation is essential if you are to teach with great clarity each step of the system. In the next chapter I will outline the procedure for preparation.

> *"As a general guide, the larger the group, the more you should prepare your class and the closer you should stick to my Stepwise teaching system."*

It is especially important to maintain good control of a large class so that everyone has the opportunity to learn (see Chapter 2 on communicating well). Be sure to make yourself visible to all, keep your instructions clear and concise and keep the class moving, without rushing. These measures will minimise interruptions. If people start losing their concentration and looking disinterested, a good way to regain control is to gently herd everybody back to practise together.

Hazel, a popular and very friendly teacher from NZ, explains how she maintains control of her class: 'I never let anyone take over my class. So when the retired CEO started fooling about, I told him (with a smile) that in my class troublemakers have to do 20 push-ups. That got everyone laughing, which drowned him out, and we carried on. When the alternative therapist started explaining (inaccurately) what he thought the movements were designed for, I told him it was fascinating, and I must ask him some questions after the class. When the "expert" asked a question, I explained the point to the whole class, rather than just him.'

Hazel's techniques work well with her experience and personality; you may have your own ways to control your classes. The key is to take control in the gentle tai chi way, that is, without confrontation, and with respect and understanding. In effect you are using tai chi techniques, redirecting and guiding the entire class to create a positive learning environment.

Hazel explains how she adapts her method to different classes: 'In a mixed ability class, I acknowledge that some students might be more 'familiar' with tai chi than others (avoid comparison or grading by not using the word 'better' or 'knows' — these words may make people who don't remember their tai chi well feel pressured), explaining to the new people that they are lucky to be in such an accomplished class, because whichever way they turn they will be able to see someone who is familiar with the form. Then I remind the seniors that although they are more advanced, it's very good discipline to break down the form into small components and take the opportunity to refine their movements.'

A small class has different dynamics and energy. You will have more time to adjust your teaching to each individual learner's style. It is a good discipline to spread your time equally among the participants and allow each person time to digest the content at their own speed. One common mistake for a novice teacher with a small class is to give too much attention to one student, which could overwhelm them. (Even if you're teaching a one-on-one class, you should avoid focusing totally on the student.) A good way is to stand back every now and then, to allow your students to have some time and space for themselves and allow you time to see the overall picture. I witnessed one diligent teacher working with one student during a private lesson recently. The teacher talked, demonstrated to the student and corrected the student's movements for the entire lesson. His eyes had never left the student. He was very dedicated, but at the end of the lesson, the student was so overwhelmed she ended up feeling inadequate, had lost her confidence and had learned little. She would have learnt more if the instructor had given her some time to work by herself, while he could have quietly observed how she was progressing, what type of learner she was and adjusted his method of teaching to suit.

New teachers often spend most of their time on the slower learners. This is not effective teaching. More instruction will not help the slow learners, rather it puts more pressure on them, and meanwhile the others get no attention, are disadvantaged and become bored.

Learn when to let go

There will be times when you have done everything and it has not worked out the way you wanted it to. This may be the time to just let go. By letting go, you stand back and let things work in their natural way. When all methods fail, let your heart take over. You can give your class a short break or just ask them to practise by themselves. You can then stand aside and quietly send your caring energy to your students.

> *"When all methods fail, let your heart take over."*

Jef Morris, a compassionate tai chi instructor, recalls his thoughts after a discussion with other teachers about teaching: '…but yet, at the very heart of it all, it is the core of your very being that we connect to in times of great fear or stress. This is why we practice, to connect with the very core of our being, and practice moving (tai chi) while sustaining this connection, without fear, without stress.'

'But just like our faith, we compartmentalize our faith, until we really need it, and we call out, and connect with it. The Truth of it is, our faith has always been there, and so is Qi. It has been said that there are as many ways to practice as there are minds to practice. When presented with someone who has not awakened to this fuller reality, we must consider that they have had this same connection with the very core of their being. It may have been through moments of prayer, driving a car or riding a bus, or just listening.'

'When we lose this connection to our very core, we can experience feelings of loneliness, sadness, a sense of being incomplete, anxiety, and even depression. So when you practice with someone who has not fully awakened, try not to find fault with them, but try to inspire them, and others, by your conduct and expression of the tai chi. Just because he may feel he cannot connect, it does not mean that you should not. Actually this begins the planting of the seeds, for bamboo shoots do become bamboo...'

One of the other instructors commented: 'It is just frustrating, that because of his faith, he questions me, I am open minded about his views, but he is not open, nor respects my views.' Another instructor added: 'It can also be the same with students. You work with them for a while, and then they stop coming... What do you do?'

Jef offered, 'Just love them.'

Adapt your teaching system to the needs of your class

You may need to adapt my teaching system a little, depending on the needs and skill level of your students. The system can be applied equally well, with some adaptation, to the teaching of new material as to the improvement of previously taught material. Because of these differences, I will explain the system for teaching new material and for improving skills (revision) separately.

Teaching new material

If you follow the stepwise method carefully, you'll be surprised how quickly your students will learn. These steps may appear too simple at first and it may not be obvious to you how important it is to understand and remember each individual step. However, it is very important; missing a couple of these steps will give you less satisfactory results. A good way to test if you have remembered them is to rehearse all the steps before you use them. You may also find it useful to remember the names of the steps in the step-by-step examples below.

> "These steps may appear too simple at first and it may not be obvious to you how important it is to understand and remember each individual step. However, it is very important..."

Toi Walker, a Master Trainer of Tai Chi for Health programs from New Zealand, describes the dramatic effect on his teaching and on his students' learning of using all the

Dr Lam demonstrates the
Wushu greeting

Above: Workshop in Indiana, USA, 2006
Below: Workshop in Sydney, Australia, 2003

Annual tai chi workshop in Connecticut, USA, 2003

*Jef Morris demonstrating tai chi for disabilities
Barcelona, Spain, 2005*

*Tai chi lesson in the park to launch Arthritis Week
Victoria, Australia, 2001*

Above: Workshop in Manchester, UK, 2005
Below: Workshop in Oslo, Norway, 2003

Annual tai chi workshop, Indiana, USA, 2006

Annual tai chi workshop, Sydney, Australia, 2005

Dr Lam with instructors of Better Health Tai Chi Chuan, 1989

Workshop in Lund, Sweden, 2003

Workshop in London, Ontario, Canada, 2004

Dr Lam, Dr Stephanie Taylor and Professor Rhayun Song at Master Trainers Workshop, 2005

Workshop in Hong Kong, 2004

Workshop in Ireland, 2004

Workshop at Monterey, USA
Dr Stephanie Taylor, Dr Paul Lam, Jay van Shelt and Dan Jones

Workshop in Seoul, Korea, 2005

Dr Lam and Cheryl Lee Player with children at the filming of Tai Chi 4 Kidz, 2005

Workshop in Wellington, New Zealand, 2005

steps of the Stepwise system: '... I would stand in front of the group with my back towards them and would do the form. I thought I was a great teacher — every time we finished the form, I turned around to the class and everyone had finished at the same time as myself, so I assumed everyone was perfect! Then I attended a Tai Chi for Arthritis instructors' training workshop in Sydney. One of the greatest aspects of the workshop was learning all the steps of the Stepwise teaching system. I couldn't wait to get home and practise what I had been taught!'

'Back home again and teaching the Stepwise way, I noticed smiles on the students' faces — their eyes were lit up, faces were glowing. "Now we know what you are doing and trying to teach us. We never had a clue before you went to your course, but now we can see what you are doing."' Toi's conclusion: 'Stepwise teaching method — just awesome!'

In order to explain my system as clearly as possible, I'll explain it from two different perspectives, starting with a general outline and following this with two step-by-step examples. The system will work for any tai chi style or forms.

General outline

I'll be using the third movement[2] of the Tai Chi for Arthritis program, *Single Whip* (Sun-style), as an example in the outline below.

Start with 'Watch me'

While facing the students, show the complete movement once, to give students an overview. Demonstrate the form without any instructions. The purpose is to give the global learners an overview, as well as to give everyone else the rhythm and feel of the form. Focus on showing the beauty of the form, to give students a kinaesthetic and spiritual feel for tai chi and to inspire them to learn. Giving instructions here could spoil the flow and may overwhelm students. It does not matter whether students follow you or not.

Tell students where the starting point is, and that you will break the movements down into smaller parts, but that you will always start from this point.

Next comes 'Follow me'

Breaking the movement into small parts, do the first part with your back to the students. Ask them to follow you three times.

Avoid turning your head too often to look back at your students during this part. If you do look back, do so only occasionally. You can use your observations to adjust your teaching. If students appear confused, break down the movement into even smaller parts. Give occasional encouragement, such as 'Well done' and 'You are doing well', as you look back. Avoid correcting anyone in this phase; do the correction later.

Emma, a caring instructor, looks back frequently during this phase. She often focuses on a slow learner near her and corrects that person frequently, while ignoring the ones she cannot see. She does not notice how most of her students are feeling uncomfortable holding in one position and are looking bored and feeling neglected, or that the student who gets all the corrections becomes overwhelmed and nervous.

Lisa, on the other hand, asks her students to hold their position between every repetition while she corrects them one by one. She often focuses on the slower learning students and offers them many corrections, as she believes that they need more help.

Focusing on the slow students is not effective. And the frequent stops hinder the flow of the teaching process.

> *"Using imagery can help learners."*

Use concise and simple instructions. Detailed descriptions can confuse some learners and are not necessary, as students can see what you are doing. I will give you a guide of what to say in the step-by-step examples later. Tai chi is an art of doing and many of the important points will become clear with repetition. Repetition builds muscle memory and facilitates learning.

Using imagery can help learners. For example, at the last part of the *Single Whip* movement, when stretching both arms out, I say to students: 'Imagine your palms are pressing on both sides of a screen door, open the door as you separate your hands.'

Last year, I was teaching at the Seoul National University in South Korea and one of the students, a professor of nursing, told me how imagery had helped her. She was having a problem remembering the sequence of a series of movements, so she started to imagine that she was playing the Korean guitar. Then she connected *Stroking Birds Tail* with carrying a plate of food, and *Repulse Monkey* with three steps back by a monkey. Using these images she made up a story about a monkey taking three steps back to bring a plate of fruit to her friend. It quickly helped her to remember the sequence — and she had a lot of fun at the same time.

Now comes 'Show me'

Turn to face your students and ask them to do the movement while you watch. During this phase, just ask your students to show you and quietly watch them. Any interruption or further instruction could disturb and confuse them. Expect your students to be able to do just the shape of the movement; leave detailed corrections for later on. Remember, no one is perfect at tai chi, let alone new learners! Over correction, as discussed in Chapter 2, can overwhelm students and impede learning. You can move on when your students are able to remember the shape of the movement. If a significant number of students don't get it, redo **Follow me** a few times and then **Show me**.

If there is an important point, especially one related to safety, that students did not do well, point this out to the students (one point at a time) and practise that point straight away. As an example, if students step their right feet out too far they could fall. Demonstrate what was wrong and how it should be done very clearly — it may be obvious to you what is right and wrong, but not to all your students, unless you make it crystal clear! Then be sure to ask your students to follow you in doing it the right way several times and check to see if it is done satisfactorily. I often see teachers bring up one point, explain what is it they want students to do, then go off to do something else. How does the instructor know if their students have understood what they meant without checking? And even if they did understand, how will they remember it without some practice? If it is a point worth bringing up, ensure that it is understood and reinforce it by asking students to **Follow me** and **Show me**.

Now they know the first part of the movement, begin again from the starting point, doing part one and then part two together. Use the **Follow me** three times, **Show me** method, as described above. When your students have learned that satisfactorily, do parts one, two and three, beginning at the starting point and using the same **Follow me** three times, **Show me** method. Continue on until you have taught the complete movement. Now is a good time to ask your students if they have any questions. While it is important to ask, don't do it too frequently or it will look like you are unsure of yourself. It also disturbs the flow if there are too many questions.

Practise the complete movement several times, alternating **Follow me** and **Show me**. It is more effective to consolidate what students have learned so far than press on with learning more movements. Trying to learn too much at a time can end up confusing students and they could then forget everything you've taught them.

> *"It is more effective to consolidate what students have learned so far than press on with learning more movements."*

When most of your students can do the complete movement reasonably well, introduce a tai chi principle that is appropriate for their level. It gives the quick learners something to extend their skills. It is also important for novice learners to know that even though by just moving their body they're getting good exercise, it is the essential principles that make tai chi almost magical in health improvement. Introduce, for example, the principle of doing every movement as though there is a gentle resistance against the movement. Show them what you mean, thn asking them to **Follow me** a few times and then **Show me**.

Later on you can go deeper into the principles. Imparting the philosophy and principles of tai chi is essential. It works better when you do this gradually and appropriately for your students' level of ability. You may find it useful reading my book co-authored with Nancy Kaye, *Tai Chi for Beginners and the 24 Forms*[3]. We explain many of the essential tai chi principles in easy to understand language. I have also included several articles about the essential principles in Chapter 11.

It is most important to help your students remember the sequence of the movements you've taught them (even just the rough shape of them), so that they can take something home to practise. Don't try to work on too many refinements of a movement, or teach too many movements, or your students may end up forgetting

> *"It is most important to help your students remember the sequence of the movements you've taught them, so that they can take something home to practise."*

the sequence. By being realistic and practising frequently with your students during the class, they have a better chance of remembering the sequence. Without remembering the sequence, they cannot practise and build on their skills.

You can do other things to help students remember the sequence. Writing down the names of the movements, with a simple description, as a handout is useful especially for the visual learners. Taping a voice calling all the movements will help the auditory learners. To help students learn, for most of my programs, I have developed teaching materials like DVDs, videos, handbooks and voice and music CDs. You can find out more information about them from my website at www.taichiproductions.com.

Step-by-step example 1

In this example I am using the same third movement of the Tai Chi for Arthritis program, *Single Whip*. For this exercise, I've divided the movement into three parts, but of course, you can divide it into a different number of parts if you prefer. Our starting point will be the end of the previous movement (we will assume students have already learned up to this point), often called the prayer position.

The starting point: with both hands in front of your chest, fingers pointing up and palms facing each other (Figure 1).

Figure 1   *Figure 2*

Part 1: Transfer your weight to your left foot. Turning your body very slightly to the right, take a step with your right foot to the right and slightly forward (a distance of about half a foot) with your right heel touching the ground (Figure 2).

Part 2: Transfer your weight forward on to your right foot, pushing both hands forward and then turn both palms to face outwards (Figure 3).

Part 3: Turn slightly to your left at the waist, at the same time separate your hands as though they are on both sides of a screen door and opening it. At the end of the movement both hands should be symmetrical, with your fingers pointing up and palms facing outward (Figure 4).

Figure 3   *Figure 4*

Step1. Watch me do the entire form

Tell students the name of the movement, where the starting point is, that you will break the movements down into parts, and that you will always start from this point. If there is a writing board handy, write the name of the movement down for the visual learners.

Say to your students that you are going to show them the entire movement and ask them to watch you. Don't say anything to them if some of them start copying you: there are always keen students or kinaesthetic learners who cannot wait to move. Unless there is some potential for injury in the movement that you need to warn them about first, it will not harm your students to follow you. Remember to do it without instructions and focus on showing the rhythm and beauty of the form.

Step 2. Follow me in doing part 1 three times

Ask your students to follow you, turn so that your back is towards the students and get your students to follow you three times. As you are leading, give simple instructions: 'Shift your weight to the left.' 'Step your right foot out.' 'Touch down with your heel.'

At each successive repetition you can vary your instructions a little, but mostly repeat the same words for consistency. If you are relatively inexperienced, practise voicing the instructions beforehand. The speed at which you talk should be same as normal talking and should correlate with your movement. In other words, choose instructions that are easy to follow and concise — just the right amount of words — so that you don't have to slow down your movement or talk quickly.

Step 3. Show me

Ask students to demonstrate part 1 to you. Remember to watch carefully without interruption or giving further instructions. Redo steps 2 and 3 if you don't think your students have learned it well enough.

Step 4. Follow me in doing parts 1 and 2 three times

Teach the hand movements separately while facing the students, because your students cannot see your hands when your back is to them. Do **Follow me** three times and **Show me** once, to ensure they have learned the hand movements. Then tell your students that you are going to turn your back to them and ask them to follow you from the starting point. Then get your students to follow you in doing parts 1 and 2 three times.

Step 5. Show me

Ask students to demonstrate parts 1 and 2. Redo steps 4 and 5 if necessary.

Step 6. Follow me in doing parts 1, 2 and 3 three times

Turn your back to your students and, beginning from the starting point, ask students to follow you doing parts 1, 2 and 3 three times.

Step 7. Show me

Ask students to demonstrate parts 1, 2 and 3. Redo steps 6 and 7 if necessary.

Step 8. Follow me and show me

Do the whole movement three or four times. Alternate between **Follow me** and **Show me**. Remember consolidating one movement is more important than learning many movements.

Now you can encourage any questions. After your students have grasped the sequence and the shape of the movement, teach them the appropriate essential principles of tai chi.

Step-by-step example 2

Now we are going to do *Waving Hands in the Cloud*, Yang-style, the third movement of the Tai Chi for Diabetes program. This movement is also a form in the most popular 24 Forms and is in other Yang-style sets. In this example, I am going to teach the upper and lower body movements separately and then combine them together. You can use the same rationale to work out the steps for any tai chi movement. With very long or complex movements, such as Yang-style's *Stroking the Bird's Tail*, you could divide the movement into more segments.

The upper body movements can be divided into three parts as follows:

The starting point: as in example 1 — both hands in front of your chest, fingers pointing up and palms facing each other (Figure 5).

Part 1: Turning your body slightly to the right, turn your right palm to face inwards and move it to the right side. Bring your left hand down to 10 cm below the right hand and turn your palm inwards at the same time, so that both palms are facing inwards, as though you are gently embracing a young child on your right side (Figure 6).

Figure 5

Figure 6

Part 2: Turn from your waist to the left and move both arms to the left, and then turn your left palm outwards, as though gesturing for someone to stop (Figure 7).

Part 3: Bring your right hand up and your left hand down, turn your left hand so that both palms are facing inward (as though you are embracing a young child), turn from your waist to the right and bring both arms to the right. Then turn your right palm as though gesturing for someone to stop (Figure 8).

Figure 7

Figure 8

The lower body movements are as follows:

Part 4: Transfer your weight to your right foot, stepping out to your left a distance that is comfortable for you to do. Transfer your weight to your left foot; step in with your right foot to a distance approximately two fists apart (Figures 9 and 10).

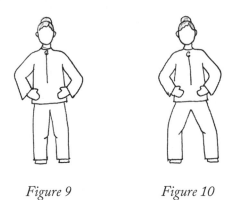

Figure 9   *Figure 10*

Step1. Watch me do the entire form

Tell your students the name of the movement and where the starting point is. Explain to them that you are going to show them the entire form once and then you will teach it in smaller parts.

Show the complete form facing your students. Ask them to watch you, but don't say anything to them if some of them start copying you.

Step 2. Follow me in doing part 1 three times

Ask your students to follow you. Turn so that your back is facing the students and get them to follow you three times. As your hands might not be visible to some students, turn you body at an angle so that students can see you better. If you have a large class, move around to different positions so that all can see you.

Give simple instructions: 'Turn your body slightly to the right'; 'Bring both hands to the right, both palms facing inwards.'

Step 3. Show me

Ask your students to demonstrate part 1 to you. Redo steps 2 and 3 if necessary.

Step 4. Follow me in doing parts 1 and 2 three times

Tell your students you are going to turn your back to them and ask them to follow you from the starting point, then get the students to follow you in doing parts 1 and 2 three times.

Step 5. Show me

Ask students to demonstrate parts 1 and 2. Redo steps 4 and 5 if necessary.

Step 6. Follow me in doing parts 1, 2 and 3 three times

Starting from the starting point, turn your back to your students and ask them to follow you doing parts 1, 2 and 3 three times.

Step 7. Show me

Ask students to demonstrate parts 1, 2 and 3. Redo steps 6 and 7 if necessary.

Step 8. Follow me in doing part 4 three times

Starting from the starting point, put your hands on your waist and ask students to focus on their foot movements and follow you three times.

Step 9. Show me

Ask students to demonstrate part 4. Redo steps 8 and 9 if necessary.

Step 10. Follow me doing the whole movement

Ask students to follow you in doing both upper and lower body movements together three times.

Step 11. Show me

Ask students to show you the movement, repeat steps 10 and 11 if necessary.

Step 12. Follow me and show me

Do the whole movement three or four times. Alternate between **Follow me** and **Show me**. Ask if there are any questions and use the questions to assess your effectiveness in teaching this form. After students are able to remember the sequence, teach them appropriate essential principles.

Improving tai chi

Tai chi is both a mind and body exercise and it has great depth. Moving the body mindlessly is not doing tai chi: when the movements are integrated with the essential tai chi principles, that makes tai chi. Integrating the principles is so vitally important that learning the right way to teach them is essential. Teaching tai chi like Kay's teacher does — trying to impart too much information and without taking the time and using the appropriate methods to incorporate the essential tai chi principles — will not work.

> *"As a teacher you need to understand the material and integrate it into your own practice before teaching it."*

Teaching is more effective if you teach 'the learner's way'. The material you teach must be relevant to and understandable by your students. Stimulating your students' thinking is more effective than spoon-feeding them, and slow and thorough teaching is more effective than rushing through a lot of material. As a teacher you need to understand the material and integrate it into your own practice before teaching it. If you just regurgitate words learned from your teacher or a tai chi book without understanding them, you will not teach it well.

Learning tai chi is a continuous process of improvement. No one does tai chi to perfection; so you don't need to understand the principles you are going to teach to their deepest level. You need only to understand them to the level your students are working towards. For example, moving smoothly is an essential principle; if your movements are more jerky than your students, it will be difficult to impart that principle effectively.

The great thing about tai chi is that, unlike many other sports, anyone can progress to a higher level, no matter what their age or physical condition. For example, in tennis after 30 you are considered to be too old and your level is expected to go downhill from then on. With tai chi, you can continue to go uphill, regardless of your age and physical condition. The secret is with the tai chi principles: understanding and integrating the principles into tai chi allows you to progress regardless of your age and physical condition. This is because mental and physical maturity is a great advantage in gaining insight into the principles. The enjoyment of practising tai chi and progressing with it is the ultimate experience that tai chi has in store for us all — a challenge and enjoyment that we as teachers can pass on to our students.

Regular practice is the key to improvement and enjoyment. Professor Vince McCullough said: 'Practice does not make perfection, perfect practice makes perfection!' Effective teachers help their students find better ways to practise, which makes their progression easier and more enjoyable. In Chapter 2, I discussed how, as part of being an effective teacher, you can help students enjoy regular practice.

The *Stepwise Progressive Teaching System* is effective for improving tai chi, but with some variations to the steps previously outlined for new material. There are two approaches to improving your tai chi:

- improving the external forms, and
- improving the internal components.

I will outline both approaches separately, although they are not really separable. Like yin and yang, external forms and internal components are integrated and inter-related in tai chi. Separating and then combining these components are, however, necessary steps for teaching. Also, at this phase of learning, you need to be more flexible in the way you teach, and use your experience and good judgment to guide you.

Learning how to do the external forms of tai chi correctly is very important, as is knowing the tai chi principles. However, there's really no value in knowing the principles if you don't integrate them into the forms. I have met tai chi practitioners of many years experience who know the tai chi principle of keeping the body upright, yet they still lean backwards. This impedes the level of tai chi that they can attain. There are even some famous experts who have written books upholding the essential principles, yet photos of them still show them leaning backwards.

> *"Like yin and yang, the external and internal components of tai chi are of equal importance and complement each other."*

Like yin and yang, the external and internal components of tai chi are of equal importance and complement each other. That said, allowance must be given to inborn body contours and limitations brought about by medical conditions. Again, perfection is not possible — no one can stay absolutely vertical to the ground at all times. On the other hand, leaning back at a significant angle is an impediment to qi flow and tai chi progression.

In improving the external forms, focus on improving one part at a time. For example, by correcting students' hand positions or body alignment.

The internal components are based on tai chi principles such as loosening ('song', relaxing and stretching out from the inside) and mental quietness ('jing', or serenity). You can find several articles on the tai chi principles in Chapter 11: *Tai chi principles*.

The ultimate aim of both approaches is to integrate the tai chi principles into the external forms. The principles cannot be integrated well if the external forms are not correct, and without the principles, no matter how exact the external forms are, they cannot be considered to be tai chi.

I find it useful to mix both approaches in one session. The Stepwise system focuses on one point of improvement at a time and follows it up immediately with practice. Before you go through any points of improvement, choose them carefully. Is this point appropriate for the level of the class? How important is it? Do you have time to go through it properly in this session? If not, choose only the point that is important and that you have the time to teach properly. Ask yourself why your students must know this point. For example why should they move slowly? And then tell your students the reason. For example, at the beginner's level, moving slowly enables them to focus on doing the movement correctly and learning to relax.

One day I saw Jack, a good natured teacher who always tries to please all his students, revising the 24 Forms set with his students. He picked the movement *Stroking Bird's Tail*. He showed one point about using the waist to control the warding-off arm, then moved on to demonstrate the weight shift at the time of roll-back and ended with showing the direction of the push. These are three very important points. While his students were still trying to understand the three big points he had given them, he asked them to start practising another movement *Waving Hands*. I was left wondering why he bothered to teach those points? He had no way of knowing if his students had understood them, as he had not asked them to show him the movement.

After students understand a principle, they need time to practise it and absorb it. In that session all Jack managed to do was confuse his students. A more effective way would have been starting with point one, using the waist to control the warding-off arm. Then, after a clear explanation and demonstration, getting his students to follow him and practise a few times, then asking them to show him. After the students had shown a good understanding of the first point, he could move on to point two in the same way. Take care not to do too many points in the time available.

Improving external forms

Step 1: Show me

Find out where your students are in their tai chi forms (following the tai chi principle of listening to the incoming force). Start by watching your students perform the movement/s for revision. A good way to prepare for this is to ask them to practise the movements with you first so that they know what they've got to do. For example if your goal is to improve the first six movements of Tai Chi for Arthritis, practise these movements with your students. Practising with students will improve their forms even if you do it without giving any instructions.

Then ask your students to show the movement/s to you. Watch your students carefully to assess their ability and work out a realistic goal for the session.

As an example, let's say you taught *Single Whip* in your last session and are going to improve this movement in today's session. (The same principle would of course work for any other movement.)

Tell your students your goal for the session. For example, to gain more health benefit by improving their forms. Watching the students, you may find the following points need improvement.

In Part 1

- Stepping their right foot out too far.
- Stepping forward instead of to the right.
- Incorrectly transferring their weight — shifting their weight forward prematurely.

In Part 2

- Pushing their hands forward too early.
- Pushing their hands in the wrong direction.
- Not turning their palms out.
- Incorrectly transferring their weight.

In Part 3

- After opening (stretching) their hands out they did not end up in a symmetrical position.
- Their palms not facing forwards.
- Their fingers pointing sideways instead of upwards.
- Incorrectly transferring their weight — instead of keeping their weight on their right foot, they transfer their weight back to their left foot.

Be realistic about what you can improve in one session. Don't try to do all of them. Remember, if you try to correct too many points you may end up achieving less.

Pick the three most important points for improvement. Let's say you have picked these:

Point1: In Part 1 — stepping their right foot out too far.

Point 2: In Part 2 — incorrectly transferring their weight — shifting their weight forward prematurely.

Point 3: In Part 3 — incorrectly transferring their weight — instead of keeping their weight on their right foot, they transfer it back to their left foot.

I would work on the first point first because it has more potential for causing injury — students can lose their balance by stepping too far. A movement that is potentially dangerous should be your top priority for correction. I chose the other two points because they are more important for progression than the others, taking into consideration the skill level of the students. It is important to balance the challenge with your students' skill level. Giving your students a task that is too difficult to correct can overwhelm them and put them off, while one that is too easy would be boring.

> *"A movement that is potentially dangerous should be your top priority for correction."*

Step 2: Watch me

Tell your students that you would like them to improve the first point and explain the advantages. Stepping closer will give them better balance, which is safer and also more effective (better balance gives stability and strength). Explain and demonstrate the movement, making it very clear which is the more desirable and less desirable way. Keep your discussion to this point, avoiding bringing in any other points that might distract them.

It's all right to be a bit more blunt when talking to a group of students; as long as you are not unfriendly, it should not cause anyone to go into their personal shell. In contrast though, be aware that pointing out a mistake in a forthright manner to a single student could put that person into their personal shell (see Chapter 2 for more information about 'personal shell') and could impede effective teaching.

Step 3: Follow me

Turn your body so that your back is to your students and ask them to follow you in doing the Part 1 movement the better way. Do it three times.

Step 4: Show me

Turn to face your students and ask them to show you Part 1. Use your discretion in judging how good is good enough.

If some students don't seem to get it, try not to single out one person; go through **Follow me** and **Show me** again with everyone. If you must correct individually after that, do so discreetly and with minimum fuss. For example, as you walk past that person while the group is practising, speak softly to them, saying 'Feet closer'. Then watch the person do it the right way, smile and give an encouraging nod. It also softens the impact if you correct a few people in a row instead of just one person.

If you know that you have some sensitive learners or students who believe they are better than they really are, be even more discreet.

When everyone has done this right, move on to the next point, using the same system. It is a good idea not to select more than three points for improvement in one session, depending on the difficulty of the points and the skill level of your students.

Final step: Follow me and show me

Practise the entire movement, alternating **Follow me** and **Show me**, to consolidate the improvement. If you think they are ready, do the internal components as below.

Improving internal components

The integration of tai chi principles into the forms takes time, patience and motivation. The principles have many layers of depth and can take a lifetime to implement. Some people may be put off with the prospect of 'devoting' a lifetime to something. Explain to your students that tai chi is an art that can enhance our whole life. We can choose to put in as much or as little as we like, but we will get back far more than we put in. Present this to your students as an advantage. Tell them they'll learn much and get a lot of enjoyment out of working with the principles. Encourage students to enjoy the journey, rather than saying, negatively, you will never reach the ultimate peak. In the journey of exploring the depth of tai chi, at every little step forward, the scenery gets more beautiful — your mind becomes more serene and your body stronger. Every little step brings great joy.

For a regular class it is a good idea to work on one concept per session. All principles have different layers of depth, so it is important to work on the level that is appropriate for the class. For example, at the beginner's level, working on doing the forms at the same speed is appropriate. As students progress into the advanced class, you could bring in the concept of variation in speed (for more about this, see Chapter 11). If you teach both concepts to beginners it might sound contradictory and lead to confusion.

> *"We can choose to put in as much or as little as we like, but we will get back far more than we put in."*

The principles may sound easy, but to truly understand them is not. True understanding can only come from regular practice. As your tai chi level improves you will find somewhat different meanings for each of the principles. Just reading about the principles from a book or listening to a teacher is not sufficient: practising integrating them into the tai chi form is the only way to truly understand them. Regular practice with a good understanding of the principles, is the only way to absorb them properly.

The most effective way to teach principles is leading by example. Practise until you understand the principle (it does not matter if you don't reach the deepest layer, as long as you have a personal experience of the level you are going to teach). Demonstrate the principle with your mind and body and your teaching will be much more effective. Learners can pick up intangible vibes from your energy.

Have a realistic expectation of your students. A beginner is unlikely to perform the tai chi movement with an even speed and the right rhythm. Jose, an extremely stressed student, had great difficulty in slowing down. I asked him to bring his hands down from shoulder height to waist height (as in the Yang-style *Commencing Form*), counting 1001, 1002, 1003 and 1004 at a normal speaking speed. Usually by the time I said 1001, his hands had already come down to his waist. It was a major difficulty for him to do something that was simple for others to do. Yet he is highly intelligent and able to do very complex tasks in his work. We settled at a realistic goal for him;

whenever he moved slowly enough for his hands to reach his waist by the time I counted to 1002, I gave him a genuine compliment.

Integrating principles can be done with one form, several forms together or a complete set. I will outline the steps you would take for a group who have done the complete set of 12 movements of Tai Chi for Arthritis. The same principle will, however, apply to any other set or style.

Step 1: Show me

Find out what stage your students have reached. This step is the same as explained previously. You can start either by watching your students perform the 12 movements, or you can practise with them and then watch carefully, to assess their ability and work out a realistic goal for the session.

Let's say you find 5 points to improve:

1.   Movements are not even in speed.
2.   There's lots of stopping and starting instead of continual movement.
3.   Lack of inner force.
4.   Not focused enough.
5.   Too tense.

For a beginner's class, the most important point here is 5, because if you can help students to relax they will enjoy their tai chi more. When students are less tense they are also less likely to injure themselves. Once they learn to relax, the qi will flow better and the other points will be easier to learn.

Step 2: Watch me

It is essential for students to understand what the principle is and why it is useful to them. For example, how does this principle improve their tai chi? Your students will also need a practical way to implement the principles and a method to check if they are doing them correctly.

Tai chi is an internal art, aiming to using the mind to control the movement of the body. Tell your students that when they are more relaxed it is easier for their mind to control their body. If they learn to practise tai chi without undue tension, it will also help them to relax in their daily life. A good way to relax is using the minimum strength necessary to move.

Demonstrate what you mean by showing how it should be done. Do just enough of the movements to show your point, rather than doing the whole set. Then involve your students by practising the set with them. When students are just watching a long demonstration, they may get bored, especially the kinaesthetic learners. If a teacher's tai chi skill is far ahead of their students, a long demonstration could overwhelm them. One of my friends, Reed, a very keen golfer, told me this interesting story about why he stopped playing golf. One day as he was playing along, a young teenager asked if he could join him for a round. Using only one iron borrowed from Reed (golfers usually use many different size clubs to get the best shot in different situations), this young man showed superb skill, scoring much better than my friend did. His skill was so superb that Reed felt that he would never come close to that. Since then my friend has lost his zest for golf.

> *"Do just enough of the movements to show your point, rather than doing the whole set."*

Demonstrate enough for your students to understand your point. Focus on inspiring your students with your demonstration of the point of improvement rather than showing them more difficult movements that you can do but your students can't. Margaret says about her teacher Bruce: 'People were always asking him to demonstrate things and his style had something to it that was inspiring — reachable — possible. It wasn't a case of, "Wow that is wonderful to watch — I will never be able to do it". It was, "That was great and I can do it too."'

Step 3: Follow me

Turn your back to your students and ask them to follow you 1–3 times, in this case the entire set. The number of repetition and forms depends on your students' progress and the difficulty of your chosen principle.

Step 4: Show me

Turn to face your students and ask them to show you. Use your discretion in judging how good is good enough. Explain the principle again if necessary. Repeat step 3 again. You can alternate **Follow me** and **Show me**, providing your students with feedback about how to do it better.

Bear in mind that when your students are learning a new principle it will take time for it to soak in. Work towards understanding the principle rather than being able to execute it well, because it will take time to be able to do that. Be aware, also, that for a while it is possible for students to appear less smooth, as they are trying to break old habits and figure out a new way to do things. I often warn students about this possibility and that sometimes it is necessary to take a small step back before leaping forward.

Step 5: Follow me

Practise with your students to consolidate the principle. If appropriate move on to the next principle, starting again from step 1.

More hints on using the Stepwise Progressive Teaching Method

Keep your students moving as much as possible, so that they don't lose their concentration or get bored or distracted. Emphasise the importance of practice. Do your best to enhance your students' enjoyment in practice, including using the techniques I discuss in Chapter 2.

Some students appreciate being challenged, especially the more advanced students. Use your judgment to reach a balance between giving a sufficient challenge for some of your students without overwhelming others.

For example, in teaching your students to apply internal force in their movements, explain how to do it in a way that students of different levels can understand and implement. For the benefit of your less able students, but without making it obvious that you are addressing them, reassure your class that this is a task that requires much time and practice. Suggest they view this as a fun activity, without any pressure to be able to do it straight away.

In more intensive classes, you could do more. The important point is to teach one principle at a time; explain and demonstrate what it means and practise that principle straight away, checking to see if it has been understood before moving on to the next principle. Sometimes it may help to provide time for your students to practise by themselves under your supervision, so that they can internalise what they have learnt.

> *"Keep your students moving as much as possible, so that they don't lose their concentration or get bored or distracted."*

In 'Exploring the Depth of Tai Chi for Arthritis' workshops, I take the participants through the essential principles one by one. The participants of my workshops usually come with a wide range of tai chi skills, from novice to very advanced. By using this teaching method I have found that no matter how advanced some of the participants are, they still gain significant improvement in skills and insight by working through principles that they must have known of for years.

Over the years I have done a lot of teaching of the Tai Chi for Arthritis program. It is a simple program and only takes two minutes to complete the set. I would do the same set many times every day. I have also taught these seemingly basic essential principles numerous times. At first I thought that it would be boring to do the same thing so many times. The fact is, my tai chi has improved beyond my dreams, mostly through these workshops. While teaching, I would demonstrate the movements, applying the principles I was teaching. For example, each time I talked about moving smoothly, I would monitor myself to see how smooth I was as I led the practice. These principles took on subtly different meanings each time I worked on them. That is how I have gained a significant improvement in my skills! You can use the same approach to improve your tai chi.

This is, I believe, the challenge of tai chi: through constant repetition and the application of seemingly simple principles we can grow and improve indefinitely. Naturally, the more advanced you are as a tai chi practitioner and teacher, the more you understand the simplicity of these principles and their immense depth, and the greater is your enjoyment.

Working with more advanced students

As your students become more advanced, encourage them to develop the ability to work out for themselves how to progress toward their tai chi goals. Helping them to think for themselves is more useful in the long term than just telling them what to do.

The key point is to help students take a positive approach to self-appraisal. Help them to identify and cherish their strong points and not to dwell on their weaknesses. When they have acquired this skill and the correct mindset, they will be able to develop their tai chi to a higher level much more quickly. Caroline Demoise, a dedicated and insightful teacher, often says tai chi is the best art for nurturing of the 'Self'. Self-growth is dependant on positive self-appraisal.

> *"...help students take a positive approach to self-appraisal."*

'Traditional' teaching is based on correcting mistakes and little or no attention is paid to what has been done well. This negative-based approach does not work as effectively as the positive approach. I often find students correct their mistakes automatically when they feel confident and are practising with a positive frame of mind, and they progress much faster when they use a positive approach. An example I often see, is that students have difficulty achieving an upright posture when they are concentrating on correcting it, but when they feel good about their tai chi, their posture often straightens out without them thinking about it.

A major barrier to positive self-appraisal is self-doubt. 'Traditional' training focuses on fixing mistakes, which often gives the impression that everything in tai chi has only one 'absolute truth' — if you don't do it this way, namely my way, then you won't be doing it correctly and you will be wasting your time! Many students ask me which way is the 'right' way because they don't want to waste their time practising the 'wrong' way. Students are sometimes told by their teachers that what they have been doing for years with other teachers is totally wrong — imagine their disappointment and how this will set back their self-confidence! The fact is, there is no absolutely one best way to do a certain thing in tai chi — but there can be many better ways.

For instance, in Yang-style, you move forwards and backwards by lifting your foot just off the ground and touching it down, like a cat. In Chen-style, you step forward, brushing your foot on the ground and often stamping noisily. It can be quite off-putting to see this if you have been told for many years that the 'right' way is to lift your foot up to step forward. But should you say all Chen stylists are wrong?

This type of dilemma makes some of us wish we lived back in the olden days, when there was only one absolute truth and only one best teacher. However, not only can we not go back in time, but also we now know that there never was one absolutely true way, nor one best teacher. In ancient times these ideas persisted because people did not travel around much and there was no way of recording teachers in action to compare them and their techniques.

After you have nurtured your advanced students to develop their skills in positive self-appraisal, you can help them to work out how to direct their learning. It is important that your students are aware of their goals in learning tai chi. Most people are learning tai chi for better health. Being healthy means being stronger internally and externally, that is, having a stronger and better-balanced body and mind. Students then can direct their learning towards those aspects that will be more effective for achieving their goals. For example, how important is it for them when doing the *Lowering* movement in Yang-style (also known as *Snake Creeping Down*) to achieve a very deep knee bend? If they balance the benefits gained in terms of better health against the potential for injury, they should see that a deep knee bend is really not important.

Encourage your students to use their understanding of the essential tai chi principles as a foundation to venture out, try it out, test it out and then use their thinking abilities to figure out what works best for them.

You can help your students choose the better options among many choices by giving them some guiding principles, such as the following ones.

Balance

The very core of tai chi is balance, balance of movements, of yin and yang and of internal and external. Movements that are either too soft or too harsh are not well balanced, and a movement that causes you to stretch so far that you nearly fall is not good tai chi either.

Dan tian

The dan tian is the centre of the body and the storage house of qi. It is three fingerwidths below the belly button and slightly inwards. No matter what style of tai chi you practise, it is essential that you have an awareness of dan tian and of sinking qi to the dan tian. As a general rule, if you find that a particular technique does not help you to become more aware of the dan tian, nor help you, directly or indirectly, to sink qi to the dan tian, then it is probably not worth doing. For more information about this, see the article about the four essential concepts in Chapter 11 and also my article with Dr Yanchy Lacska, reprinted in Chapter 12.

Practice

One of the absolutely 'always stays true' principles of tai chi is practice. No matter how bright you are, how good your method of tai chi is and how much you understand the theories, if you do not practise, you will never truly understand the inner meaning of tai chi and you will gain little or no benefit.

Integration

By integration I mean that whenever you move, your mind and body are fully integrated. At any given point in time, the hands, body and feet should all move in a fully coordinated way, from one position to another. As one part of the body moves, the rest follows. The mind drives the qi and the qi moves the body, integrating with the movements.

Working with other teachers

Whether you are working with a colleague at the same level as yourself, a senior teacher or an assistant teacher, working with another teacher can be a challenge. If your collaboration works well, you'll achieve greater goals than the sum of both people working on their own could ever do. So it is worth putting in the effort to learn how to do it effectively. I will provide a few simple points here, as the full topic would require another book.

> *"Show respect to your colleagues regardless of seniority. Avoid contradicting your colleagues in front of students..."*

- Show respect to your colleagues regardless of seniority. Avoid contradicting your colleagues in front of students, even if it is a trainee instructor. If you want to say something to them, do it in private, and do it using the same rationale as I outlined in Chapter 2 — start with a positive statement, give only one point of improvement and watch out that you don't push them into their personal shells.

- Have a meeting before you work together, working out who is to do what and how. Decide on a lead person who is responsible for the overall operation and who will assist. This role can be changed in the next session. As part of the training of our Tai Chi for Health master trainers, they go through a mentorship program with a senior master trainer before they go out on their own. In these sessions, they switch leading roles in alternative sessions, so that attendees do not know who is the mentor and who is the mentee. We found this most effective and beneficial for mentors, mentees and attendees.

- After a session, meet again to discuss what was done well and what can be done better. Our Tai Chi for Health master trainers meet before and after our workshops. Both mentor and mentee write a report for me, which helps all of us improve our effectiveness.

- The lead teacher should be considerate of their assistants, dividing the tasks during a class so that all the assistants are involved.
- Consult each other during the class; for example, at an appropriate time you can ask if your colleague has more points to add to yours.

Chapter 6
Organising your class

Developing a good structure for your classes is as important for their success as a good framework and solid foundation is for a building. In the previous chapter, I discussed my system for teaching. In this chapter I will discuss the practical issues of:

- how to prepare for your classes;
- class format; and
- follow through.

These two chapters work hand in hand.

Preparing for your class

Preparation involves setting up your classes, marketing and financing them and getting ready for your class; planning your lessons and rehearsing them.

Setting up

Who might be interested in your classes?

Working from the end result you have in mind, decide what kind of students you would like to work with before you go and find them. Ask yourself these questions: Do you enjoy improving people's health? Do you enjoy working with older people? Do you prefer working with martial artists?

"Working from the end result you have in mind, decide what kind of students you would like to work with before you go and find them."

Hazel Thompson from Christchurch, New Zealand, an experienced teacher who really cares about elderly people, says this about her class: 'It is important to remember though, that you are dealing with intelligent, often highly qualified people and you should not just categorise them as elderly.' You can see that Hazel respects and enjoys working with older people. No wonder her classes are always full and her students love her.

Keith's main interest, on the other hand, is martial arts and he is impatient with most students — only a very few students can learn quickly enough to meet his expectations. In an effort to get more students, he has tried to teach people in a retirement village and even the general public, but it was not an enjoyable experience for him or his students and, not surprisingly, he now has only a few of these students left. Keith has now stopped teaching tai chi for health; he specialises in martial arts students.

When you have worked out what you want to achieve and who you enjoy teaching then you have the direction to reach your students.

Where will you have the classes and when?

This depends on the type of students you are looking for. For health improvement, an ideal room size will include a space of 5 feet x 3 feet (1.5 metres by 1 metre) for each student (15 square feet/student or 1.5 square metres/student). Many people work with much less space, especially in most of my Tai Chi for Health programs — the sets are simple and less space is required. It also depends on what space is available and how flexible you and your students are.

Use your experience and the rough guide of 5 feet x 3 feet for each student to judge what is the right space for your class. A good way is to see the venue before starting, do the tai chi set you are going to teach there and visualise the maximum number of students you might have doing the set with you. That should give you an idea if the space is right.

It is best to hold your classes in a building that has adequate parking space and is not too noisy. Be sure there is a telephone for emergencies and convenient bathrooms (see Chapter 4: *Safety first* for other safety precautions). Steps are a challenge for people with arthritis and it is best to avoid venues that require participants to go up steps. Good lighting and easy transport are also important factors.

Church, school and community halls can be suitable. Be sure to check out everything about the venue before starting.

How much 'ownership' you have of the venue will determine how much you can and want to do to create an appropriate ambience for your class. For example, if you rent a church hall once a week then you have less ownership than if you have exclusive use of your own hall. Do your best to decorate the hall as it will enhance your effectiveness. Keep the decoration simple and let it reflect tai chi's serenity, feel and heritage. Be sure it doesn't obstruct your lessons or distract your students. A banner or a notice board, perhaps with a picture of yin yang on it, might be enough. Cheryl, the artistic tai chi teacher, has painted several figures of people doing tai chi on one wall of her class hall. You may find ways that appeal to you and achieve the same purpose. It is important that your venue reflects your professionalism — make sure it's clean, tidy and has a warm feel.

Appropriate music can add ambience and help students appreciate the rhythm of tai chi movements. Some music resonates with tai chi better than others. I have a specially commissioned CD of music, composed to correlate with four tai chi styles and based on their individual rhythm and feel. If you buy it through my website it has special rights that allow you to use it for your classes and performances without paying any extra fees.

> *"The best advertisement is word of mouth..."*

Classes are usually 45–60 minutes in length and the time of day you hold them should be student-orientated. For example, people with arthritis and seniors often like to gather mid-morning, about 10–12 pm. That is often when they feel most energetic and more mobile. Working people naturally prefer their classes in the evening.

How to market your class

Work out a marketing plan. If people don't know about your class you won't have a class, no matter how good you are. Here's some ideas for spreading the word about your classes.

Use word of mouth

The best advertisement is word of mouth — talk to your friends, personal contacts, local community and work colleagues. And remember to ask them to spread the word around as well. You may be surprised at who might come to your class. I remember an obstetrician, who everyone thought was so busy he would not consider coming to a tai chi class. We sat next to each other at a social dinner, talked about tai chi and in five minutes he was enrolled. On the other hand, be wary of over-pushing your class — salesmanship can turn people off. The key is to provide accurate information and proven benefits.

Have a flyer or brochure printed

A flyer or brochure is a necessity. Make it simple and give the essence of what you are going to teach, including why people would want to take the course and, most importantly, how they can benefit from coming to your class. Give your credentials without it looking like you're showing off. Most tai chi teachers are enthusiastic about teaching tai chi, but they can get a little caught up in how advanced their tai chi is, and how much they know. Many times I've heard teachers spending a long time telling their class how many forms they know and how great are their skills.

Be careful not to over emphasise the difficulty of tai chi as this can scare students off, as happened with Kay's teacher. Tai chi is often completely new to people, especially the elderly, and they want to be reassured that you are teaching something they can do that benefits their health. Be sure to include where, when and how to contact you. I provide a sample brochure in the Appendix at the end of this book.

Contact health care professionals and seniors groups

If you want students who are looking for health improvement, you could contact healthcare professionals, seniors centres and fitness trainers in your area and leave your brochure and contact details for your class. Especially encourage people who have found other forms of exercise difficult to try tai chi. Family doctors, clinics, physical therapists and seniors clubs or groups are excellent sources of referrals.

Give talks to local groups

Offer to give a talk at your local golf club, social club, doctors' meetings or local community activity groups. I will provide a guide to public speaking in Chapter 9.

Contact your local newspaper

Your local newspaper is a good place to advertise your classes. Keep your advertisement brief, focus on what benefits students can get and include your contact details.

Your local newspaper is also a good source of free publicity. Newspapers love to report things that help people in the community, especially if you approach them the right way. I will provide a guide to working with the media in Chapter 9.

Use the power of the internet

On my website I provide a free service for any tai chi teacher to post information about their services online. Many people search the website for tai chi teachers: in July 2006 we were getting around 1500 hits every day. Debbie, who teaches tai chi full time, told me that all her students came from either word of mouth or website referrals. To enter your name on my website, go to www.taichiproductions. com and click on the link 'Instructors', then follow the directions. Of course, after you get established, if you're knowledgeable about computers you may want to set up a simple website of your own promoting your classes.

Finance

If you can afford to teach tai chi free — great. You are contributing to society in the best possible way I know. However if you wish to spend more time teaching, it may be necessary to get some remuneration for your time. Don't be shy about it

> *"In considering the financial aspect, think of how much time you can spend and how much you need to be compensated financially."*

— be upfront and confident that you deserve your payment. I admire tai chi teachers because I firmly believe that one of the greatest contributions we can make to our society is to help improve people's mental and physical health. When a person becomes healthier and happier, they will interact with others with more gentleness and care, and gradually the ripple effect grows. In our special way, we, as tai chi teachers, can make the world a nicer place to live in for our children and for ourselves. The service we deliver is very valuable.

In considering the financial aspect, think of how much time you can spend and how much you need to be compensated financially. Work out the expenses of running the class and a realistic income from it. Take time to plan your budget and revise as you go. A talk with your accountant or financial adviser is worthwhile.

It works better to charge students per term rather than per session. People are more likely to turn up if they have already paid for the term. Many schools give a discount for paying by the term and an extra discount for paying by the year. Our school charges by a term of two months. We offer a free first lesson and give a greater discount to students who join up for one year.

As the world begins to recognise tai chi as one of the most effective and enjoyable exercises for improving health and quality of life, the demand for tai chi teachers has never been so high and so our opportunities to reach and help more people is certain to increase.

I have taught tai chi free for many years and still do, along with my colleagues, in our school *Better Health Tai Chi Chuan Inc* (a registered non-profit organisation). About ten years ago, in order to devote more time to tai chi, I decided to work outside my school as well so that I could charge for my time. It was very challenging to find tai chi work that paid me close to my hourly rates as a successful physician. It did take time to build up, especially when people were used to me donating my time free for so many years! Now I'm established, I have more work than I have the time to take up. My success came from improving the value of my service. I utilise my unique qualifications and experience to deliver more value than I am paid for. For example, many research projects employ me as a consultant. My service includes designing the program, training the instructors and advising on the study's design. I combine my medical, tai chi, exercise and research knowledge to enhance the success of these projects. Government departments in different countries have recognised the value of my work in health improvement. People travel around the world to attend our workshops year after year because I provide teaching that is great value for the cost. You too, can improve the value of your service in your own unique situation. Give it time and you have a good chance to be remunerated at the rate you deserve.

The health-giving effect of tai chi is increasingly being recognised. There are more opportunities to make teaching tai chi a possible dream career. What can be more fulfilling than helping people to improve the quality of their lives?

In recent years many federal and local government bodies, charity organisations, workplace organisations and other communities and societies throughout the world have sponsored tai chi at one level or another. For example, the Accident and Compensation Corporation of New Zealand (ACC, a national government body) has paid for 10,000 elderly citizens to attend tai chi classes throughout New Zealand in the year 2005.

In the USA, Tai Chi for Health Community is a non-profit organisation aiming to bring tai chi for health programs to as many people as possible. In Australia, the Tai Chi Association of Australia, as part of its mission, has set out to facilitate teaching tai chi as a profession — a necessary step in bringing tai chi to more people. Join an organisation relevant to you, as working in a group can be more effective than by yourself.

Getting ready for your class

Getting ready for your class involves getting to know your students, planning your lessons and rehearsing them

Get to know your students

Find out the composition of your class and your students' possible objectives for taking it. You could be like Chaz, who rings all new students before their first lesson to welcome them, tell them what to expect and offer any assistance they may

"Find out the composition of your class and your students' possible objectives for taking it."

need. In doing this, Chaz also finds out a lot about them, which will help him adjust his plan and make his class more successful. There are other ways you can find out as much information as possible, to help you prepare for a successful class.

The way you promote yourself will attract certain types of students. For example, if you distribute your brochures in a retirement village or doctors' waiting rooms, you are more likely to get elderly students for health improvement. Our surveys have shown that most people who enrol in tai chi classes are over 50 years old and the vast majority of them are joining to improve their health and relaxation.

You could use your enrolment form to ask prospective students what their objectives are in learning tai chi and other useful information you wish to know about them. Be sure to look at the forms before you plan your lessons. I provide a sample enrolment form in the Appendix to this book.

Plan your lessons

Have your students' objectives firmly in mind when planning your lesson. It is better to teach less at a rate that can be absorbed comfortably, rather than so much that students are hard pushed to learn it all in the time available. It is not how many forms or sets of tai chi students can learn; rather it is how well they have learned it that determines how much enjoyment and benefit they will gain from it. As a rough guide, an appropriate amount for most classes is to teach one or, at most, two new movements in a lesson of one hour. I have included a sample first three lessons in Chapter 7: *Getting started*. This will give you an idea of what you should cover in your classes in Sun-style tai chi. In my *Tai Chi for Beginners and 24 Forms* book, I have also included a lesson plan for beginners for Yang-style tai chi.

> *"Have your students' objectives firmly in mind when planning your lesson."*

Be prepared for unexpected challenges and to be flexible in your plan. In any given life situation there is only one possibility that things will turn out just as you planned, but there are hundreds of ways it can go wrong. If things do go wrong, complaining and finding a scapegoat is a negative reaction, which at best is a waste of time. You can analyse it later, to learn from the experience and avoid it happening again. The key is to adjust your teaching by revising your plan whenever necessary, with the aim of fulfilling your students' objectives as much as possible under the changed conditions.

A lesson plan is not necessarily limited to any set time. A tai chi lesson can be done in almost any length of time. In full-day workshops, we schedule lots of rest periods during sessions. Even in a one-hour lesson for the elderly, it is a good idea to schedule a ten minute rest half way through.

Sometimes you will have the opportunity to present a very brief trial lesson, which can be a great way to introduce tai chi. Last year I was asked to give a 15-minute presentation to a group of 600 delegates of the 31st Annual Meeting and Exhibition of the American Association of Diabetes Educators in Indianapolis, USA. I planned the presentation very precisely to make use of every second. I divided it into a 7-minute PowerPoint presentation to introduce the topic of Tai Chi for Diabetes, then for the last 8 minutes I asked all the delegates to stand up in the lecture hall and gave them a brief tai chi lesson. Some of the educators enjoyed it so much that they later came to my workshop.

In the next section I am providing a suggested format for a class; you can use it in planning your lesson and modify it to meet your needs. In your plan, be sure to factor in time to allow for slow learners or unexpected interruptions.

At the beginning, students often have difficulty acquiring the habit of regular practice at home. Many people come to a tai chi class and do nothing in between, as though they are working out in a gym. Allow time for students to understand the importance of home practice and to cultivate the habit. Plan your lesson to allow adequate time to go through the forms and the sequence often enough so that students can still remember them at the next lesson. If you teach students too many forms, they are likely to forget the ones you taught them before and will start to feel lost. When students feel lost they are unlikely to enjoy the wonderful feel and rhythm of tai chi and will probably drop out of the class. If you can keep them interested until they start enjoying tai chi and its benefits, then there is more chance they will acquire the habit of regular practice.

Rehearse your lessons

Write down your lesson plan and rehearse it. A good way to rehearse it is to teach family members or friends. By trying it out you can find out if your plan is realistic — use a stopwatch to time yourself. Alternatively do a rehearsal with an imaginary audience or do a mental rehearsal. Even if you are an experienced teacher, it pays to rehearse. I have taught my Tai Chi for Health workshops numerous times; I still find rehearsal helps to improve my lessons.

> "Write down your lesson plan and rehearse it."

Rehearsal also includes practising the forms that you are going to teach: if you are not familiar with your forms, you will not be an effective teacher. When Pat Webber, a very experienced master trainer of the Tai Chi for Health programs, teaches a class she views my instructional DVD/video as part of her preparation, even though she already knows these forms very well. The reason why Pat is so effective is that she is so well prepared at whatever she does. All my instructional DVDs include details of how to break down each movement into steps that can easily be learned. (Also see Chapter 5: *The Stepwise Progressive Teaching Method*, which gives the reasons for breaking down the movements into steps and tells you how to go about it.)

A good rehearsal makes for a successful lesson. The time spent in preparation is well worth it. The more you prepare, the more effective you will be.

Class format

The duration of a class depends on the type of students you are teaching and the time available. For example, older people may not be strong enough to exercise for one hour. Judy is a fitness leader and a tai chi teacher who enjoys working with older adults. For her elderly students, she splits the one hour into three sessions, 20 minutes tai chi, 20 minutes rest and then back to tai chi for 20 minutes. Sharon, who teaches tai chi to primary school children, breaks the class into half an hour of tai chi, half an hour playing games and then back to another half an hour of tai chi.

One hour is usually a convenient length of time for most classes, so I will base my guide below on this; however do adjust it according to your situation. The times given below for each stage of the lesson are suggestions only. You will need to vary them depending on your situation. This guide is for teaching less experienced students; as students become more advanced, the format becomes more flexible. Always consider your students' level of skill and objectives when working out your lesson plan. By the time you are teaching advanced students, I am sure you will have acquired the skill to work out what works best for them and for you.

Stage 1 Getting connected (1-5 minutes, but longer for the first lesson)

It very important to start off by establishing a good relationship with your students, being connected, as it were, in a mind-to-mind sense. Often taking just a brief moment to do this will stand you in good stead. An excellent starter is to say hello, with a smile, and give a brief introduction of yourself and what you have planned for this lesson. For the very first lesson, a good way to get connected with your students is to ask them to introduce themselves. Be sure to give them a clear guide of what and how much you want them to say. People can get carried away talking about themselves, which could disrupt your schedule. For a tai chi for health class, for example, you may wish to say to students: 'Would you like to tell us briefly your first name, where you come from and what you would like to get out of attending this class?'

Hazel, the teacher from New Zealand, says: 'I do like to get people to introduce themselves at the first lesson and often find I have retired teachers, swimming instructors, health professionals and many other interesting backgrounds.' Getting connected is about developing a friendly and interactive relationship with your students.

In subsequent classes, getting connected at the beginning of the lesson may only take a brief moment. It could be a reminder of what was taught at the last lesson and what is in store for this lesson. Another good way is to ask if anyone has practised or do they have any questions for you. Cheryl an experienced and innovative teacher from Newcastle, Australia, often challenges her students jokingly to make an effort to forget what they have learned. Her connecting question at the next lesson is, 'Have you all forgotten what we have learned from the last lesson?'

> *"A formal greeting that establishes mutual respect is useful to set the tone of the class."*

Hazel often tells her class that there are two rules in her class: 'One is to have fun and the second is to take care to be safe.' This is an excellent connecting talk — brief, useful and setting the right atmosphere.

A formal greeting that establishes mutual respect is useful to set the tone of the class. We use the official greeting of the International Wushu Federation. (Wushu is the Chinese term for martial art, of which tai chi is a major branch.) It is an effective way, taken from Chinese traditional training, to get connected with your students.

Tell students about this etiquette of greeting each other at the start and finish of each class. Then explain the meaning of the greeting gesture. (There's a photo of me demonstrating this greeting among the colour photos in the middle of this book.)

- The right fist is clenched to denote strength.
- The left thumb is bent to denote humility.
- The other fingers of the left hand are held straight and close to each other, meaning friendship.
- The two hands are held together with the right fist on the left palm. In sum, a greeting to show mutual respect.

Stage 2 Giving a brief talk (3-10 minutes)

This can be given at the beginning, or in several small segments throughout the lesson, depending on the level of your students and other factors. It can be about basic theory, tai chi principles or general background information. After the first few lessons, you can combine this stage with revision. As you work with your students, you will get an idea of what theory may benefit them most. You can integrate it with practice to improve their skill. For example, if many of your students are simply moving their hands and arms mindlessly, talk to them about how to focus, using their mind to direct their movements. Then practise doing that with them.

Be aware that talking for more than five minutes at one time can be too long in an exercise class. Tai chi is an art of doing: sometimes too much theory can be confusing and lead to negative results. You might feel good about sharing your tai chi knowledge, but if your students are not ready or able to receive and absorb the knowledge, they will feel overwhelmed and frustrated. I met Ron two years ago, a tai chi scholar who studies tai chi theories fervently. Unfortunately he does not practise regularly. Therefore his form of tai chi does not in any way reflect his 'book' knowledge. This knowledge remains 'book' knowledge to Ron as, by not practising, he has never gained a real understanding of the principles nor their health benefits. No one becomes proficient in tai chi just through 'knowing' the theories.

A talk for the first lesson could be as simple as this: 'Tai chi is a gentle exercise that originated from ancient China and is especially beneficial for health. One of the most effective ways to do tai chi well and build internal strength is to do all your movements slowly and gently.' This gives the historical background to tai chi, mentions one of its essential principles and explains why it is important (all appropriate at a beginner's level) in less than 40 seconds.

Another talk for the next lesson could be: 'You might find the lesson slow to start with, because I believe in building a good foundation. With a good foundation, in the long run you will gain more health benefits and learn more. Patience is also part of the essential tai chi training.'

Remember that older people and people with arthritis can't stand up in one position for a long time and that people tend to lose concentration after the first ten minutes of a talk. Keep your talk to a minimum. Tai chi theory is very important but only if it is relevant to your students' level and if it can be integrated into their practice. Too much talk without practice will not make a student understand what tai chi is, nor will it improve their health or their form. The tai chi principles will reveal themselves through regular and correct practice.

The principles to be talked about in subsequent lessons could be:

1. Maintain an upright and relaxed posture at all times.

2. Be conscious of and clear about weight transference.

3. A 'bent-knee' stance is desirable but students must work toward it gradually, starting with their knees only slightly bent.

Read the previous chapter for information about how to integrate theory with practice. You can also use the tai chi principles listed in Chapter 11 for your talks.

Stage 3: Warming up and stretching exercises (8-15 minutes)

Warming up is important to prepare your students for their lesson. It gets the body and mind ready for learning, and the muscles and ligaments warmed up and stretched to prevent injury.

> *"Warming up is important to prepare your students for their lesson."*

You may have your own favourite warm-up routines, but be sure to check with an exercise or health professional that your routine is safe for your students (see Chapter 4: *Safety first*).

You can use my 'Step 1–2–3' warm-up and cooling-down system, which is explained in Chapter 8. I have worked with many tai chi and health colleagues to develop these exercises. They are easy to learn, more interesting than the usual warm-up exercises and incorporate tai chi principles. You can use it in your class without applying to me for copyright. However, it is your responsibility to take care to teach it safely and to modify it if appropriate for your situation. You can learn it from any one of the Tai Chi for Health training workshops run by myself or one of my authorised master trainers. A detailed description of these exercises, with photos, is included in my book *Tai Chi for Beginners and the 24 Forms* and the instructional DVD, *Tai Chi for Beginners*.

Stage 4 Improving skills or revision (15-20 minutes)

Revise what you taught your students in the last lesson. If you are teaching a set, it is a good idea to go through the whole set from the beginning, up to where you finished and then focus on the less well-performed parts, in particular, the material you taught in the last lesson. My system, the *Stepwise Progressive Teaching Method*, gives a practical method for improving skill through revision. If you have not read it, please go back to Chapter 5 and do so. The key is to assess your students' present skills (in terms of tai chi technique, 'listening to the incoming force'), find out what would help them best to progress in their tai chi journey, and assist them to make this progression toward their goals at a realistic pace.

Giving your students a brief break from formal teaching when appropriate helps them to relax and enhances the friendly interactive atmosphere, which in turn facilitates learning. In some traditional tai chi classes, smiles and laughter are forbidden, which creates an overly strict atmosphere that significantly impedes many people's ability to learn. Margaret tells us about her teacher, Bruce: 'He was a great storyteller. His stories were either interesting, thought provoking or amusing. He made us smile a lot!' Hazel from New Zealand explains that: 'I often tell my students funny tai chi stories, or make a joke at my own expense during class — if you can get them all laughing together then they are well on the way to being a group, rather than a collection of strangers.' Hazel also uses music that resonates with the students as a bonus break from tai chi. She says that when she does this, they often will break into a spontaneous dance, which they all enjoy and adds to the friendly atmosphere in the classroom. A good break is brief and, in some way, contributes towards helping your students reach their objectives.

Stage 5 Learning new material (15-20 minutes)

My system, the *Stepwise Progressive Teaching Method* (outlined in Chapter 5), gives a practical and comprehensive method for teaching new material. If you have not read it yet, please do so before continuing.

Have your lesson plan ready but be prepared to adjust your plan if necessary. If you notice that some students are getting tired, have a brief break in the middle of the class. Alternatively, you can carry on teaching with your students sitting down (this works particularly well for the first 6 moves of the program Tai Chi for Back Pain). A lesson while sitting down not only gives your students a break from the usual lesson, but also can help them to focus on different aspects of tai chi. This method is not just useful for students with disabilities, but can be helpful to all your students, because people learn different aspects of tai chi from different approaches.

Grace planned to teach the movement *Stroking the Bird's Tail*, Yang-style (the 7th movement of the 24 Forms or the 15th movement of the Tai Chi for Diabetes program) in one lesson. She was very committed to the plan, so she pressed on even though her students were not learning it as fast as she expected. To make sure that she finished teaching the entire movement in the lesson, she had to cut the number of teaching steps. At the next lesson, she found out that most of her students couldn't remember much about this complex movement. Grace realised her original plan was too ambitious, so she went back to square one, starting to re-teach the movement step by step according to the Stepwise method.

She would have done better to modify her plan during the first lesson as soon as she saw that her students were struggling to learn it. That way her students would have learned less but retained more and the next lesson would have been made much easier.

This illustrates the importance of following the *Stepwise Progressive Teaching Method* without skipping any of the steps. The good thing about this method is that it makes the learning process easy so that students can feel good about their ability to learn. When they see themselves as able learners, they learn faster in future lessons. Do you remember the self-efficacy model of Professor Albert Bandura, which I discussed in Chapter 5? Mastering a skill gives a learner confidence, which leads to more successful learning in the future. Rushing through a learning task is not effective because students do not learn well and end up feeling inadequate as learners.

Stage 6 Cooling-down exercises (5 minutes)

Doing cooling-down exercises serves to relax your students, loosening their muscles and ligaments and preventing injury. Recent studies have shown stretching, as a form of cooling down at the end of an exercise session, helps better retention of flexibility gained from the exercise.

Please note my 'Step 1–2–3' routine, outlined in Chapter 8, includes cooling-down exercises.

Stage 7 Ending on a positive note

Rick, a teacher from Colorado, USA, always likes to have his students leave his class on a positive note. He often asks students if they have positive stories to share. Many students have experienced the health and personal benefits of tai chi and they enjoy sharing this with others. People get inspired by hearing personal stories, especially from someone they know. For many people, this provides a good incentive for regular practice.

Lynne has had three anaphylactic shocks (a fatal form of allergic attack), which required resuscitation in intensive care units of different hospitals. In her words, 'I died three times'. As a result, she started having anxiety attacks when travelling. She always wanted to visit her sister (who cannot travel due to illness), who lived in another state of Australia. After learning tai chi for one year, she developed the courage to try it. The first lap was a flight to Sydney. Something happened that day and the airport was chaotic and Lynne nearly went into a panic attack in the crowded airport. She found a seat, sat down, closed her eyes and started visualising going to her tai chi class and doing the entire session. After that she opened her eyes, felt calm and was able to continue her journey. She came back to tell her class about the episode and everyone was so touched they all ended up in tears. Lynne has had a special glow about herself since then and everyone in her class was inspired by her story.

Real life experiences like this inspire and motivate the whole class. Even if not done regularly, sharing positive experiences is a good thing to do every now and then.

Stage 8 Positioning students ready for their next lesson

Leave your students something to look forward to in their next lesson. For example, you can demonstrate the form they will be learning in the next lesson. Keep it brief and enticing rather than making it look so complex that they get the impression that they have no hope of achieving it.

> *"Leave your students something to look forward to in their next lesson."*

You can set students some 'homework', but make it subtle by using another name for it, otherwise it could remind them of school time. For example, ask your students to spend five minutes a day revising what they have learned. Make the homework easy and fun and students are more likely to do it. Cheryl's homework for her students is for them to try to forget what they have learned in the lesson. She figures people are more likely to remember if she asks them to try to forget. It works well for her. Hazel asks her students to incorporate tai chi into their daily lives. She says: 'When you do the dishes, use a tai chi stance, and when you walk, think of the weight transfer and body alignment.' I often ask participants of my workshop to use imagery to revise the material learned as soon as they get home. For more about this, read the article *Enrich your Tai Chi Practice with Imagery* by Dr Yanchy Lacska and myself in Chapter 12.

You could also ask your students what they wish to practise before the next lesson and how much time they will allocate to this. This encourages them to set their own goals and follow through with them. And when they do so, remember to give them your enthusiastic praise.

Professor Song from Korea has success using contracts to increase compliance of practising tai chi. She says: 'We use the method of making contracts. The individual writes a promise on their daily exercise log, let's say that they will practise for 30 minutes a day, 5 days a week, then signs it and submits it to their leader. The leader checks each week to see if they have actually kept their promise. This is a simple way to motivate people and to enhance their compliance.'

Follow through

All tai chi movements have an initial part, leading to the main component and then a follow through part, like the parts of a tai chi symbol that together make a completely whole and powerful movement. The structure of a tai chi class works similarly: preparation is the initial part, class format is the main part and follow through makes a complete whole.

Follow through starts from near the end of the lesson and leaves the students well positioned for their next lesson.

Work out appropriate ways to encourage your students to practise regularly between lessons. For example, Hazel encourages her students to incorporate tai chi practice into their daily lives. With my own class, I encourage students to allocate a regular time daily for practice, even if its only ten minutes and slowly build it up to 40 minutes on most days. Studies have shown 40 minutes of moderate exercise on most days gives a dramatic improvement in health and quality of life. A powerful way to encourage regular practice is to give appropriate positive feedback.

Our school has allocated free time for students to practise, under minimum supervision. We also have a free monthly practice in the park and twice a year intensive workshops — all different follow through choices for students.

Design your curriculum to offer students follow up courses. For example, after the beginner's class, we offer the 24 Forms. After they finish the 24 Forms, they can choose to explore further the depth of it or start learning the 42 Forms. For the program Tai Chi for Arthritis, as a follow up to Part I, we offer Part II and then a class on Exploring the Depth of Part I and II, to be followed by the 73 Forms. You could make up a list of other tai chi teachers who specialise in different areas and who you could refer your students on to. If you cannot help your students fulfil their objectives, it is better to refer them elsewhere — in the long run, you will gain more students by putting their interests first.

If students do not attend a class, it is an excellent form of follow through to ring them and find out why. Be sure to do so with the right intentions and with tact. A good way is to show that you care by asking them if they are all right and if there is anything you can do for them.

You can encourage students to form 'buddy' groups to practise together during the week and to check on each other if they miss class. Dr Aeyong Eom from Seoul, Korea, asks her class to form several buddy groups. The buddies encourage each other, help each other and call each other if one does not turn up to a class. This brilliant idea helps students to learn more quickly, develops strong bonds between students and enhances their chances of persevering with classes. This is part of the reason Dr Eom has a very high retention rate — a result that is especially important as her class was part of her research study on the effect of tai chi on breast cancer.

> *"Encouraging social interaction is another excellent form of follow through."*

Encouraging social interaction is another excellent form of follow through. Our school has regular social gatherings, such as at mid-year and at Christmas. Many of our students are like members of a big family; they draw support and strength from each other.

An integral part of follow through is to use a feedback form to find out your students' opinions about how the class went and what can be done to improve it.

Helping students to see the eventual health benefits of doing tai chi will enhance their commitment to your class. Sometimes people are impatient or don't understand how tai chi help can improve their health. Teachers like Bruce, Margaret's teacher, help students understand the health benefits of tai chi: 'He was clearly committed to and totally convinced that tai chi was beneficial and he passed that on to everyone — he would tell stories about the benefits, but in a way that didn't make you feel like you were being lectured — he just opened your mind to possibilities — you always came out feeling uplifted by doing something good for yourself.'

If you know of a student who has a serious medical condition, it helps to give this student hope. You don't need to be a doctor to give people hope. Many studies have shown people will do better by feeling more positive about themselves and their health. For example, several studies have shown people with breast cancer achieve better health outcomes by being positive. You don't need to promise anything, just encourage hope and tell them about the health benefits of tai chi, especially the benefits proven by scientific studies.

Be aware of your students' financial commitment when attending your classes and, if they are regulars or assistants, show them that you appreciate it. For example, many schools offer a significant discount for returning students. Some teachers take their regular students for granted. My friend Bill was an assistant teacher, but he continued to pay full fees. He did not mind paying fees and did so for many years until one day the teacher's accountant sent him a rude letter because he had unknowingly missed paying his fees. That is a very impersonal way to tell someone who has given you so much loyalty and support. Let your regular students and assistants know your appreciation for their loyalty and support in any way you can. A good way is to give them discounts, certificates of achievement or of appreciation, a scholarship or any other form of genuine encouragement. Your caring attitude will help to keep your students coming back.

How to motivate students to stay on and to practise

A major part of follow through is to inspire and motivate your students. Teach in the way your students learn best and help them to feel good about themselves. Having the right attitude and helping students to enjoy their tai chi and to understand its benefits are all good motivators. I have discussed these and other methods of how to motivate and inspire your students in detail in Chapter 2.

PART 3: THE TOOLS

By now you will have tried out my teaching method and will have an understanding of the theory behind it. Very likely you will have found that you and your students are now enjoying your tai chi more and progressing well with it. If, however, you have not yet read Parts 1 and 2 of this book, please consider doing so, from the beginning.

This part of the book is like a treasure chest or toolbox. In it is collected a variety of useful material that I have developed over the years. The chapter on the first three lessons is to help you quickly get started with the Tai Chi for Arthritis program, if you really don't have the time to go through the book from the beginning. The 'Step 1–2–3' warm-up and cool-down system in Chapter 8 is an integral part of all of my Tai Chi for Health programs. You will learn it from attending any of our training workshops.

In Chapters 9 and 10 you'll find ideas and advice on dealing with the media, public speaking, publicising your classes and collaborating with research projects.

Chapter 11 contains a collection of short articles about tai chi principles. There are many well-written books and articles about tai chi principles, but I have summarised the essential principles for you. Throughout the book I have quoted these principles to illustrate certain teaching techniques.

In Chapter 12, you'll find a collection of 'gems' from my teaching colleagues — articles they've written about teaching tai chi effectively. I'm sure you'll find them both interesting and useful.

The material in Part 3 is all useful, though for different purposes. Feel free to pick and choose any of these topics that interest you and read them in any order you wish.

Chapter 7
Getting started:
The first three lessons

A suggested format for the first three lessons, based on the Tai Chi for Arthritis program.

General guidelines

1.   Be sure to go back and read Parts 1 and 2 of this book from the beginning as soon as possible.

2.   Before you start, make sure you've covered all the safety precautions outlined in Chapter 4: *Safety first*.

3.   Learn the *Stepwise Progressive Teaching Method* (see Chapter 5) and how to organise your class (see Chapter 6).

4.   Work with your students; find out their needs and their physical condition. It is much better to work with them rather than talk down to them.

5.   Encourage your students to practise regularly, ideally for 30–40 minutes a day. It can be done in separate sessions.

6.   Try not to criticise your students. Give them positive feedback whenever appropriate and always substantiate it. For example, saying 'You are very good' has little meaning if you don't point out what is good. Try to say something like, 'Your movements are slow and gentle. That's very good.'

7.   Keep corrections to a minimum; think of them as points of improvement. Never give more than one point of improvement at one time, and make sure it is accompanied by positive feedback, given both beforehand and afterwards, if possible.

8.   Keep your talk to a minimum. Tai chi theory is very important, but too much talk will not make a student understand what tai chi is, nor will it improve their health or their form at tai chi.

Also theory must be relevant to the students' level of tai chi and be easily understandable.

9.   Before you start, consider asking your students to sign a release form and, if required, get a doctor's written clearance.

10.   Remember to rehearse your lessons. Time yourself at the rehearsal.

Lesson one

Welcome (20 minutes)

Introduce yourself. Give a brief statement of your credentials and focus on what benefits students may gain from coming to your class. For example, the Tai Chi for Arthritis program is shown by scientific studies to improve arthritis, balance and other health factors, so your students can expect to see health improvement within three months.

Ask students to introduce themselves. Give a guide to what they should say. For example, 'Please tell everyone your first name, where you are from and why you have come?' Consider using name tags.

Greetings

Use a simple greeting at the beginning and end of the class. You can use the official greeting in the Wushu world, as described in Chapter 6.

Warm-up exercises (10 minutes)

Use the 'Step 1–2–3' system which is an integral part of the Tai Chi for Arthritis program (as updated from 2001) and is explained in Chapter 8. If you are teaching another set of tai chi forms, you may use the Step 1–2–3 system for warm-up if you wish.

Suggested talk (5 minutes)

Tai chi is a gentle exercise that originated from an ancient Chinese martial art. It's especially beneficial to health. One of its major characteristics is control of movement; it's important to move slowly and gently in order to generate internal strength.

Explain that learning tai chi may seem slow to start with. Ask students to be patient with themselves and with you, to allow time to build a good foundation for their tai chi. By doing this, they will gain more health benefits and will enjoy tai chi for a longer time. Patience is also one of the essential principles of tai chi.

Lesson (15 minutes)

Using the *Stepwise Progressive Teaching Method*, teach Movement 1, *Commencement Form*. I will provide a brief outline of the steps involved here but be sure to read and understand the full method as detailed in Chapter 5. You can refer to the Tai Chi for Arthritis instructional DVD/video if you are not familiar with the movements and breakdown of parts.

Step1. Watch me do the entire form

Step 2. Follow me in doing Part 1 three times

Part1: Hands up to shoulder height and down to near the dan tian.

Step 3. Show me

Ask students to demonstrate Part 1 to you. Redo Steps 2 and 3 if you don't think your students have learned it well enough.

Step 4. Follow me in doing Parts 1 and 2 three times

Part 2: Hands up along the chest and then push forward.

Step 5. Show me

Ask students to demonstrate Parts 1 and 2. Redo Steps 4 and 5 if necessary.

Step 6. Follow me in doing Part 3 three times

Learn the foot movements separately.

Part 3: Left foot forward and then bring the right foot to be alongside the other, a shoulder-width apart.

Step 7. Show me

Ask students to demonstrate Part 3. Redo Steps 6 and 7 if necessary.

Step 8. Follow me doing Parts 1, 2 and 3 three times

Combine both body and feet movements.

Step 9. Show me
Ask students to demonstrate Parts 1, 2 and 3. Redo Steps 8 and 9 if necessary.

Step 10. Follow me and show me
Do the whole movement three or four times. Alternate between **Follow me** and **Show me**. Remember, consolidating one movement is more important than learning many movements.

Now you can encourage any questions. After your students have grasped the sequence and the shape of the movement, teach them the appropriate essential principles of tai chi.

Cooling-down exercises (5 minutes)
Doing cooling-down exercises serves to relax your students, loosening their muscles and ligaments and preventing injury. My 'Step 1–2–3' routine, outlined in the next chapter, includes cooling-down exercises you can use.

Lesson two

Greetings

Suggested talk (2-5 minutes)

Moving smoothly
It's important at this beginning stage to think about controlling the speed of your movements so that they are smooth or even in speed, and as slow as is comfortable for you without stopping.

Warm-up (10 minutes)

Lesson (40 minutes)
How you will allocate your time during the lesson will depend on your students' progress. Usually revision takes about the same time as teaching new material. Many people come to a tai chi class and do nothing in between, as though they are working out in a gym. Allow time for students to understand the importance of home practice and

to cultivate the habit.

Do as much practice as possible and keep students moving most of the time; you'll find this is usually an effective way of teaching. Practising during the class will help them to feel the nice rhythm of tai chi and familiarise themselves with the sequence of movements. It is important to help students remember the sequence and encourage them to practise at home.

Revise lesson one — see Chapter 5 for techniques for revision or improvement.

Teach the following new content, depending on how well your students have learned the previous lesson. If they are slow learners, do one movement only. If they are fast learners, do more revision and work on moving smoothly, but don't teach them more than two new movements. Use the same rationale from the *Stepwise Progressive Teaching Method* for your teaching:

- Movement 2 *Opening and Closing Hands*
- Movement 3 *Single Whip*.

Cooling-down exercises (5 minutes)

Ask for questions and suggestions

Follow through

As outlined in Chapter 6, give them some simple homework and demonstrate what they will be doing the next week.

Lesson three

Greetings

Suggested talk (2-5 minutes)

Balance

It's important to have mental and physical balance. Tai chi is especially effective for both. Physical balance is the balance you must maintain as you move, for example, as required by Movement 4 *Waving Hands*. Maintaining good physical balance will improve muscular strength and minimise falls.

We will discuss mental balance in more detail later; for now you should work on focusing on your tai chi and not allow other things to distract you.

Warm-up exercises (10 minutes)

Lesson (40 minutes)

Revise lessons 1 and 2.

Teach Movement 4 *Waving Hands*. This can be divided into two lessons if some students have difficulty mastering it.

Cooling-down exercises (5 minutes)

Ask for questions and suggestions

Follow through

Homework and what will be happening next lesson.

Chapter 8
'Step 1-2-3' warm-up and cooling-down exercises

I have spent close to two years working with my tai chi and health professional colleagues to develop a set of safe and comprehensive warm-up, stretching and cooling-down exercises. The 'Step 1-2-3' system incorporates essential tai chi principles and is easy to learn and remember. These exercises will prepare your students for their class, helping them to orientate their mind to tai chi, minimise injury and improve flexibility.

Start by learning the shape of the exercises, then do Step 1 (warm-up) and Step 2 (stretching) before you start teaching and Step 3 (cooling-down) before you finish your class. When you become familiar with these exercises, you can develop tai chi depth within them and, if you string them together, it is a nice set of tai chi forms. For more detailed information read my book co-written with Nancy Kaye, *Tai Chi for Beginners and the 24 Forms*, available from my website at www.taichiproductions.com. We have also produced a wall chart of these exercises to help you remember and teach them.

You can use my system in your class without having to apply for permission or a licence, although you must take care to teach it safely. Use the system entirely at your own risk. You can learn this system from any of my Tai Chi for Health instructors' training workshops run by myself or by my authorised master trainers. A calendar of the workshops can be found on my website.

When teaching these exercises, remember to always do the easy alternative first. Ask your students to do the more difficult movements only when they are comfortable with them. If you have any students who you think may need support, suggest they use a chair or wall whenever they need it. It is a good idea for you to use a chair to set an example.

Step 1: Warm-up exercises

For one or two minutes, walk around, gently shaking your hands and legs, and clenching and unclenching your hands. This loosens your body and joints and starts the blood circulating in preparation for the exercises that follow.

Step 2: Stretching exercises

Tai chi principles are integrated into these exercises. Practising them regularly will enhance your flexibility and tune up your muscles.

- Do all movements slowly, continuously and smoothly.
- Move well within your comfort range. The first time you do a movement, stretch to only 70 percent of your normal range of motion and increase that range gradually.
- When appropriate do both sides.
- Do each stretch 3–5 times. It doesn't matter which side you do first.
- If you have any difficulty balancing, use a chair or the wall for support.
- We're going to gently stretch six parts of the body — neck, shoulders, spine, hips, knees and ankles — with two stretches for each body part. It might help you to remember them by knowing we are working from the top down, starting with the neck, and ending at the ankles. It is quite all right if you prefer to work from the feet up.
- Unless otherwise specified, keep your feet a shoulder-width apart.

Neck exercises

1. Head down
As you inhale, bring both hands up slowly, imagining your wrists are being lifted by two balloons.

Turn your palms so that your fingers are pointing upwards. Bring your palms towards your chest and push your chin (or your head) gently backwards.

Exhaling, push both hands outwards, extending them in front of you, and then press your hands down slowly and gently. At the same time, slowly bring your head down towards your chest.

2. Turning head

Starting the same way as in the neck exercise, lift up both hands, then turn your left hand so that your fingers are pointing up and your palm is facing you. At the same time, gently push your right hand down so that it is near the hip with the palm facing down. Look at your left palm.

Move your left hand to the left, turning your head slowly to the left and keeping your eyes on your palm. Then come back to face the front. Change palms so that your right palm is now facing you and the left is down near the left hip. Turn to the right while looking at the right palm.

Shoulder exercises

1. Shoulder roll

Roll shoulders gently forward three times and then backward three times.

2. Gathering qi

Inhaling, extend both arms to the side. With palms facing up, move your arms up in a curve to above your head.

As you exhale, gently press your hands down in front of your body to below your navel.

Spine exercises

1. Spine stretch (Heaven and Earth)

Hold your hands in front of you, one hand above the other, palms facing, as though you're carrying a large beach ball. Inhale.

Exhaling, push one hand up as though your palm is pushing against the ceiling. At the same time, push the other hand down by your side — imagine stretching your spine gently. Then change hands.

2. Spine turn

Hold your hands in front of you, as though you're carrying a large beach ball, with the left hand on top.

With knees slightly bent, turn your waist gently to the left. Then change hands, putting the right hand on top and turn to the right. Keep your back upright and supple, being sure to turn no more than 45 degrees from the front and turning from the waist rather than turning from the shoulders. To check that you are not turning too much to the side, look down at the end of the turn; your palms should not be outside a straight line from your palms to your knee.

Hip exercises

1. Forward stretch

Bend your knees slightly and step forward on your left heel. Push both hands back to help your balance.

Step backward with your left foot resting on the toes, stretching your hands forward at about shoulder height for better balance. Repeat on the other side.

An easy alternative: Place your left foot down next to your right foot before stepping backward.

2. Side stretch

Bending your knees slightly, push your hands to the side as though you're pushing against a wall. At the same time, stretch the opposite foot out sideways. Maintain an upright posture and stretch only as far as comfortable.

Knee exercises

1. Slow kick

Make loose fists, palm-side up, resting at the sides of your hips. Bend your knees slightly.

Stretch out one foot (like a kicking motion, but slowly and gently). At the same time, punch out gently with the opposite fist, turning it palm down as you punch out. Bring your arm and leg back in and repeat on the other side.

An easy alternative: Stretch out one foot forwards so that the toes touch the ground and then bring them back. The key here is to straighten out the knees gently — a high kick is not necessary.

2. Step forward

With fists next to hips as above, bend your knees slightly and step forward with one foot.

Shift your weight on to the front leg, and as your body moves forward, punch out with your opposite fist. Bring your foot back and do the other side. Maintain an upright and supple posture.

Ankle exercises

1. Tapping

With your hands on your hips, tap the floor with your heel and then your toes. Now do the other foot.

2. Rotation

Toes down, lift up the heel and gently rotate your foot in one direction three times, and then in the other direction three times. Change feet.

An easy alternative: Turn your foot inwards and outwards several times. Avoid over-stretching by not putting weight on the turning foot.

Step 3: Cooling-down exercises

These exercises are to be used after you complete your tai chi session. However, it is worthwhile learning them beforehand so that you can do them following your very first lesson. These exercises will help to enhance your flexibility, relax your muscles and prevent injury.

1. Punching thigh

Lift your left knee to a comfortable height and gently punch the top of your thigh with your left fist. Now do the other leg and fist.

2. Tense and relax

Inhaling, clench your hands, gently contract the muscles of your body, and stand on your toes if you can.

Exhale, dropping gently down off your toes and letting everything relax.

3. Arm circles (Gathering qi)

Inhaling, with palms open and facing up, extend both arms to the side. Move your arms up in a curve to above your head.

As you exhale, gently press your palms together and down in front of your body to just below your navel.

Chapter 9
Public speaking and working with the media

A very effective way of promoting tai chi and your classes is through presentations at meetings or conferences and through the media. These opportunities sometimes land on your doorstep, but more often than not you have to go out and look for them. If you are presented with an opportunity to reach out to more people, be sure to make the best of it. It's like when students walk through the door to your class, it is an opportunity too good to be wasted. I will provide a simple tai chi-orientated guide for how to make the most of these opportunities. I have had many opportunities to speak at scientific conferences and public meetings, and have been interviewed on television and for newspaper articles and other media around the world. Over the years I have found the same set of principles work for most occasions. At the end of this chapter I will also provide some tips on how to be proactive and create these opportunities for yourself.

> *"If you are presented with an opportunity to reach out to more people, be sure to make the best of it."*

The key steps are preparation, giving your talk and following up after your talk.

Preparation

When preparing your talk, focus on the audience, what they want to know and how can they benefit from your message. People want to know that what you have to offer can benefit them — they are not interested in how great you are, but they do want to know how credible you are, that is, do you have the credentials to deliver the benefit to them?

Background information

Conferences and meetings

Get to know as much as possible beforehand about your talk. The more you know, the more likely your talk will be effective. Find out about:

- Your audience
- How many people are likely to come?
- Age range, background and interest?
- What do they wish to know?
- If it's a conference:
  - What is the theme and what topics do other speakers cover?
  - How long do you have for your talk?
  - Are there other speakers?
  - Is there an honorarium for the presentation?
  - Who do you contact to make arrangements, find equipment and notify changes?
  - What audiovisual aids are available, such as a projection system for your presentation, microphone, whiteboard?
  - What's the space you're presenting in and what are its acoustics?
  - How to get there, where to park etc.

Interviews with the media

If you're giving an interview or writing an article for the media, find out:

- What type of publication is it (eg, local or national newspaper, magazine, academic journal)?
- What's its audience (age range, background and interests)?
- What's its circulation?
- How long has been allocated for the interview?
- What's the length of the article to be published?
- Can you check the article before it goes to print?

For example, if you're asked for an article of 150 words for a newspaper or magazine, this is relatively small, so your message should be very concise. I once wrote a tiny 100-word article about the Tai Chi for Arthritis program for the Australian Women's Weekly. Our phone rang hot for days afterwards!

If you're being interviewed for newspaper or television, be aware that the time the interview takes can be very different to the length of time or space your message ends up getting. I once did a national television interview (ABC USA), which was to be aired for six minutes — the interview took three hours. My friend Nancy took a bus full of students, travelled two hours to San Francisco and was filmed for two hours — they appeared on the national television for barely twenty seconds! No matter how much or how little exposure you get, if you do it well, it will promote tai chi, bring people to your classes and help people to gain enjoyment and health benefits.

Get to know who you're dealing with

It is also important to get to know the facilitators (the reporter, journalist, photographer, meeting or conference organiser) you're dealing with. Your message will reach the audience if it is of interest to the facilitators. Find out which way is the most effective to communicate with them and respect their time and preferences. Some reporters like a written story given to them prior to the interview or a detailed press release and some prefer to start from scratch. Some are good listeners and some just push you to give them what they want to hear. A good journalist has often done their research beforehand. It is usually better to assume your reporter is knowledgeable and your audience is new to your topic. Once you get to know the facilitators, you can adjust this method as you go.

As a general guide most audiences want to know:
- What is tai chi?
- How does it work?
- How does it benefit them?
- How do they learn it?
- What does it look like and feel like?
- What do you have that is unique or different from others?

Most journalists like to include real life stories, so be prepared and have several students ready to speak to them. Readers or viewers find it easier to understand the benefits if a real person tells or shows them. On the other hand, scientific journals and governmental departments prefer published studies and frown on personal testimonials. Credibility is very important to them too, so saying something that has not been supported by published studies could affect your credibility. If you are not familiar with medical studies, ask a recognised expert to go with you.

Preparing your talk or interview

Establish your objectives: what results do you want to achieve? For example, do you want people to know about the health benefits of tai chi in general, or its benefits for arthritis or diabetes? Or are you looking for enrolments for your class?

Correlate your objectives with what the audience and facilitators are looking for, then work on the content of your message. It is also important to know what not to do. For example, some journalists don't like you to sell anything, so telling people about your class or products during the interview may worry them. Others want to provide their viewers or readers with information about where they can find learning materials and classes. Ask about this before the interview so that you can get the best outcome for yourself without upsetting the journalist. Think of your talk as an opportunity to present the serenity of tai chi through your demeanour and respect for others and you have already communicated the most important aspect of tai chi.

> *"Establish your objectives: what results do you want to achieve?"*

Depending on the time and space available, your content should have no more than three main points. If the time is limited, go for the strongest point; it is more effective than two or three rushed points. Make your points clear and straightforward. Explain simply why your audience should know these points. Start by telling your audience why your talk is important to them; if you cannot do that in less than a minute then you are likely to lose them. Trying to fit in too many points will result in no one remembering anything important at all. Talking fast and trying to fit in as much as possible will also work against you, and talking too slowly will bore them. A normal enthusiastic pace is the best. If you think you need to be seen as a credible source for this information, give your credentials simply, without showing off.

If you're talking at a non-scientific meeting, starting with a real life story often helps to capture people's attention. With academic meetings, this may also work, but you must be careful not to arouse negative feelings from scientists who do not trust testimonials — no matter how real, case histories are only personal experiences, which seldom constitute scientific evidence.

Always allow question time, as questions let you know if you are on the right track and if you are getting your message across. Don't get annoyed with someone asking you a question that you have already covered in your talk — it means you did not make the point clear enough.

In most of the tai chi talks I give, I build in a 'let us try it' session. This is a very short tai chi lesson that attendees do, standing in front of their seats or while seated. Of course, it would be great if you could arrange a room for your talk with space to move around. This has proven to be most popular on almost every occasion I've done it. At the 31st Annual Meeting and Exhibition of the American Association of Diabetes Educators in Indianapolis, USA, I was asked to give a talk for 15 minutes. I covered the two most important points:

1. What is tai chi?
2. Why is my Tai Chi for Diabetes program especially beneficial for people with diabetes?

I supported my points with reasons and scientific studies, had time for two questions and still fitted in an 8-minute 'let us try it' session. It went so well several people attended my workshop after that talk!

This case illustrates how valuable the 'let us try it' session is; it is often the part that people remember best. I consistently get excellent feedback from this session. Plan the 'let us try it' session well. Do only a few movements so that attendees can learn easily and perform the tai chi within the space available. Try to make it fun and enjoyable and aim at leaving attendees with a good feeling about the rhythm and beauty of tai chi.

Like all things in life, the promised time may not work out and the equipment can break down. So prepare your contents in such a way that you can cope with any change. I once travelled overseas for a meeting with the national manager of a government department and his staff. The time allocated for the meeting was half an hour and I was well prepared with three key points. As it turned out, we could only meet for five minutes. I was able to cut my talk to one absolutely most important point. It turned out to be incredibly successful, but if I had tried to get through my original three points in the 5 minutes it would not have worked.

> *"Try to make it fun and enjoyable and aim at leaving attendees with a good feeling about the rhythm and beauty of tai chi."*

If possible get one or two friends, who you know well enough to be honest with you, to review your talk, to ensure that what you thought would be easily understandable is indeed so. Likewise do your 'let us try it' session to ensure it is do-able within the time and space.

Rehearsal

Rehearse your talk so well that it does not sound like it has been rehearsed. Understand the material well and prepare for questions. Use your tai chi training to incorporate a jing (serenity or mental quietness) state with your talk. If you visualise your talk as real as possible and rehearse it with a calm and clear mind, chances are you will be calm during the talk.

Giving a talk or interview

Many people get nervous talking in public. There are psychologists who specialise in training people to overcome this. You may want to consider working with one of them. The very core of tai chi is developing jing, or serenity of mind, so utilise your tai chi training to help. I will offer a few hints.

- If you feel nervous, try not to focus on being nervous. Thinking about how important the talk is will only give you more pressure. Substitute any nervous or pressuring thoughts with positive thoughts, such as focusing on your topic, or do a mental rehearsal or recall a successful talk you have done.
- You may feel better to occupy yourself before the talk with an enjoyable activity, such as a walk in the garden.
- Practising tai chi is most helpful in calming the nerves. Focus on the essential principle of tai chi, put your mind in the jing state and focus on your talk. Ralph Dehner, a master trainer of Tai Chi for Health programs, is forever looking for ways to utilise tai chi. During his daughter's wedding, she became so anxious it triggered off an asthma attack as Ralph was walking her down the aisle. He supported her and talked her through tai chi breathing (she had been learning tai chi for some time by then). By the time she reached the altar she had regained her breath and her composure and the wedding went on without a hitch.
- A good way is to look at one person in the audience. Find someone who looks friendly and enthusiastic and visualise talking to him or her as if talking to a good friend. Move between 'friends', because just looking at one person doesn't look natural.

Be prepared for anything that could go wrong. I once attended a talk by the then retired Prime Minister of Australia, Mr Bob Hawke. He was giving a talk at a business executives' dinner. The people were noisy and then the microphone broke down. Mr Hawke did not show the slightest sign of annoyance. He started off as though he were speaking in the most favourable of circumstances and managed to communicate to the audience in a few sentences why his talk was important to them. Once the audience started listening to him, they fell into a complete silence, totally captured.

On another occasion, I went to a medical conference where one speaker complained about the malfunctioning PowerPoint projector at least ten times during his presentation, whch spoilt a good talk. Afterwards we happened to meet as fellow speakers, as I had done the presentation just before him. He told me how much he liked my talk and that I was lucky the projector worked well for me. In fact it didn't, but I did not complain, just found another way to move on and no one noticed it! Most people, wherever you talk, are not interested in any of your problems; rather they prefer to hear what can benefit or interest them.

In your talk, speak clearly. Put forward one point and support it: why should people remember it or why is it important to the audience? Remember your audience is unlikely to be as interested in the topic as you are. I have often heard over-enthusiastic tai chi speakers trying so hard to push people to love tai chi — only to turn some people off. If you talk about the health benefits of tai chi, support it with evidence and sound reasoning. Illustrate it if you can

> *"Most people, wherever you talk, are not interested in any of your problems; rather they prefer to hear what can benefit or interest them."*

with your personal experiences, involving yourself and your students. And, if appropriate, make it fun and entertaining; a sense of humour is a good way to open people's minds.

If there is a podium, avoid hiding behind it. If possible use a lapel microphone so that you can move around. It is more interesting to the audience to watch you in action rather than hiding behind the podium reading the speech. If you're going to do a 'let us try it' session a lapel microphone is most useful.

Have copies of an information sheet ready to give the audience. It should contain essential information, references and how to contact you.

If you are working with the print media, try to arrange for one or more photographs to be included — a picture speaks a thousand words. And for television, offer and be prepared to do a demonstration. Even in a limited space and time, you can show the beauty and serenity of tai chi. During some of my television interviews I offered to teach the presenter tai chi in front of the cameras. Most presenters took me up on the offer. It was the most effective part of the interview.

For the 'let us try it' session, or a demonstration in limited space, you can find ideas about how to do it from my DVDs *Tai Chi For Back Pain* or *Tai Chi Anywhere*.

Following up

Afterwards, have a post-mortem. Work out what you did well in your talk and where you can improve it. Revise your plan for next time — there is always another chance.

Let your assistants and any students who have testified the benefits of tai chi for you know how much you appreciated their help. Send the facilitator a thank you card or phone them, to let them know what positive results have come from the publicity. Avoid complaining about anything they did not do, but focus on the positive outcomes. If there is a new development, supply them with this information. With my Tai Chi for Diabetes research study, the journalist from our local newspaper published a follow up article about the study when I told her that we needed more subjects.

Keep a file of these contacts for future use.

Creating opportunities

Tai chi is an ideal exercise for health. With the increased ageing of the world's population, it will inevitably become more popular. The opportunity to spread the message about tai chi through meetings and the media is getting easier by the day. The key to approaching facilitators is similar to the approach you take in spreading your message. Focus on what the audience (in this case, the facilitator) wants to know, supply useful information that can benefit them and keep your message simple.

If possible explain why your message is unique and why the attendees, readers or viewers would benefit from hearing about you. The media can be challenging to access sometimes; try to approach as many sources as possible.

In the Appendix to this book, I have included the text of a letter written by Nancy Kaye, which helped her to get a half-page story in her local newspaper in Orange County, California, USA, which has a circulation of 300,000 people. Note how she stresses the benefits to the readers, and how she starts with a 'hook' of being unique ('I'm probably the only one…') to get the editor interested in keeping on reading. She then emphasises why what she has to offer will interest readers and simply states her credentials, backing it all up with evidence (the video). Nancy is a retired editor of the US magazine, *Medical Economics,* and the half-page of publicity she got from her letter helped me to fill my workshop and three of her own classes, plus a long waiting list.

The Appendix also contains a second sample letter written by me to the *Today Show* of Channel 9, an Australian national television program, after it televised an interview I did with the USA ABC's *Good Morning America*. In my letter, I emphasised the benefit for viewers and pushed Tai Chi for Arthritis' Australian connection — if *Good Morning America* had broadcast my message all over the world, why shouldn't my own country's TV do the same with Australian content? It worked: I got a ten-minute segment on the program, which led to many people knowing about my program and subsequently gaining health benefits from learning it.

Depending on your own situation, if you wish to find students for your class, then a local newspaper is a good starting point. Many teachers I know of have got good free publicity from their local newspaper, which has helped them start their classes. Most community newspapers are keen to find local stories that are positive and uplifting. However, use your imagination and try out any appropriate channel.

After sending your letter, fax or media release, be sure to follow up with a phone call after a suitable period of time — usually two or three days later. If your first attempt does not work, keep trying. Perseverance often pays off in the long run. If you have a unique program or tai chi class that can benefit people, keep telling the media, meeting facilitators and anyone you think might be interested. Sooner or later you will be given the opportunity to practise your public speaking skills.

Remember, public speaking is like tai chi: the more you practise it, the better you will be.

Chapter 10
Collaborating with research studies

If you are not a health professional or research worker, you might feel out of your depth if someone invites you to participate in a research project on the health benefits of tai chi. If you are asked to teach a tai chi class as part of a research study, you might think you don't need to know or do anything extra — you would just teach your class as normal. In a way this is correct, but to make your contribution to tai chi and science as valuable as possible, you can do much more to enhance the accuracy and effectiveness of the study.

Most tai chi researchers don't know as much about tai chi as tai chi teachers. In fact many chief investigators (most research studies nowadays are conducted by a team under the leadership of a chief investigator, who operates somewhat like the CEO of a company) know next to nothing about tai chi. I have found many researchers don't know that there are many different types of tai chi and different ways of teaching it, therefore the outcomes may not be replicable. Some people see tai chi research as the same as drug research; tai chi is treated as if it is one pill — with the same properties and side effects. In fact the different types of tai chi and the way it is taught can result in quite different health outcomes.

> *"...you can do much more to enhance the accuracy and effectiveness of the study."*

It is important to find out how much the research workers know about tai chi and help them understand your type of tai chi. Good studies have key aims; hypotheses to prove; outcome measures and a strict protocol. Find out the aims of the research project; how the outcomes are to be measured; how long the tai chi lessons will go on for and what type of subjects are going to be recruited, so that you can collaborate effectively with the rest of the research team. Try to understand as much about the research project as possible and ask for it to be explained to you in plain language. Let the chief investigator know that the more you know, the more you can enhance the study. Remember however that the chief investigator is in charge and you must work with him or her within the parameters of the study.

When collaborating with a research team, there are three key aspects to consider, namely safety, efficacy and adherence (compliance).

Safety

I once became involved in a tai chi study of elderly people with arthritis. The tai chi exercises proposed were not suitable for the subjects as they included dangerous movements, like bending with straight legs to touch the toes, and twisting the knee while most of the weight was on it. If the subjects had become injured as a result of the study, it would not have benefited either the study or the reputation of tai chi. This is why you need to know what type of subjects will be attending your classes and let the researchers know exactly what you will be teaching. Get opinions from appropriate medical experts, for example a sports physician or physiotherapist (or physical therapist), who is familiar with the area of research and tai chi.

I have outlined safety precautions in Chapter 4. Please read this in conjunction with medical advice and share it with the researchers.

Efficacy

Almost all tai chi studies are focused on proving or confirming its health benefits, so deciding what you going to teach, how you teach it and over what period of time is crucial. Many other factors within your control can influence the study's outcomes. For example if a study is done in a poorly ventilated, noisy and untidy room it will affect the outcome, and downgrades the benefit of tai chi when it is compared to another exercise conducted in an ideal setting.

I will list a few key points here as a general guide to planning your lessons to achieve appropriate positive outcomes, but each study should be considered separately, taking all factors into consideration.

Planning your lessons

Allow half the lesson time for learning new forms and half for practice and consolidation. During the learning phase, people are moving slowly and often clumsily. They cannot gain much of tai chi's benefits because they are not yet doing 'real tai chi'. The great health benefits of tai chi come from following its essential principles, such as moving smoothly, being well-balanced and having a serene mind. You cannot achieve these during the learning phase. Plan your lessons so that there is adequate time to practise the forms, so that the subjects can gain health benefits. More practice is also important to help them remember the sequence so that they can practise at home.

Allow adequate time to teach the forms well. If you try to cover too many forms and rush through your teaching, you will get worse results rather than better. Like public speaking, less is more. It is better for your students to learn less forms, and practise them regularly than learning many forms poorly.

In an ongoing class, health benefits will come eventually, so no one really notices which phase of the learning process delivers the health benefit. In a study with a time limitation, it is crucial that you plan to allow enough time for benefits to be generated before they are measured. Factor in more practice time after learning the forms. Use the practice time to improve tai chi forms through integrating the essential principles. Students will need the time and practice to gain the health benefits.

Different health benefits may take different periods of time to generate. For example, for people with arthritis, two separate studies[1] [2] have shown that three months is required to deliver the benefits of less pain, better ability to do their daily activities and better balance. When measurement was done after six weeks, no benefits were recorded[1]. Health benefits, like cardiovascular fitness, diabetes control and problems relating to chronic conditions, may take even longer than three months. Some studies are now planning to include one year's tai chi classes. This will have a much greater chance of demonstrating the many health benefits of tai chi.

Choosing the right setting for the study

To enhance the study participants' attendance rate, make the venue for your class convenient for them to attend. In one study I know of, the class was held in a venue that was almost impossible to get parking near, which meant that attendance dropped. This handicapped the outcome of the study. Be user friendly — and provide catch up lessons if necessary. It helps to have adequate space, good ventilation, a friendly atmosphere and good ambience. See Chapter 6 for more about preparing a good physical environment for your class. You will do tai chi and your research team a disservice if, through having a poor environment for your students to learn in, you end up proving tai chi does not work as effectively as it should.

Teaching methods

Consider using the teaching method I describe in Chapter 5, because it has been developed and shown to be effective at making tai chi easy to learn and enjoyable. Subjects feel more confident if they have found learning easy and enjoyable and this empowers them to learn more quickly. The more they learn, enjoy and practise tai chi, the more health benefits they will gain.

You can put more emphasis on aspects that are more relevant to the outcomes to be measured. For example, if the study is about improving balance, put more emphasis on weight transference, body alignment and mental confidence. Do more practice on these aspects. If the study concerns improving cardiovascular fitness, encourage a lower stance throughout the practice (making sure it is done well within the safety guidelines).

> *"The more you can motivate people to practise the better will be the outcome for them and for the study."*

Adherence (compliance)

If most of your subjects drop out of the class by the end of the study period, it will not reflect the truth about tai chi's health benefits and will harm the study. The more your students adhere to your class, the better the study result will be. The more you can motivate people to practise the better will be the outcome for them and for the study. This should of course be the same aim for your normal tai chi classes — you want your students to stay around and practise regularly. There are ways to improve the adherence rate. Make a real effort to learn as much as you can about ways of optimising it.

In Chapter 2 you'll find more information about how to help people enjoy their tai chi. People only keep doing things if they enjoy them. There are also ideas about how you can encourage regular practice. Incorporate as many of these as you can into your normal class as well as your research class.

Chapter 11
Tai chi principles

The essential tai chi principles

Tai chi is a sophisticated art with many different styles and forms. Despite the many variations of tai chi, its immense power for improving health and inner energy derives from a set of essential principles.

Here we present the most important ones. We've put them into simple, easy-to-understand language. By bearing them in mind as you learn and practise, you'll be able to do tai chi more effectively right from the beginning. To see if you're following these principles, you can use a video camera, a mirror, or check with a friend or instructor.

> *"Tai chi's immense power for improving health and inner energy derives from a set of essential principles."*

1. **Do your movements slowly, without stopping**. Make them continuous like water flowing in a river. Don't jerk. Maintain the same speed throughout.

2. **Imagine you're moving against resistance.** This will cultivate your inner force (qi). Imagine the air around you is becoming denser and that every move you make is against a gentle resistance — almost like moving in water.

3. **Be conscious of weight transference**. This is important for improving mobility, coordination and balance. Be aware of each step as you transfer your weight. When you move forward, for example, put your weight on one leg, while maintaining an upright posture. Touch down gently with the other heel first, and then gradually place the entire foot on the ground and

put more of your weight onto that foot, slowly and consciously transferring more of your weight forward.

4. **Maintain an upright posture and body alignment**. It is important that you maintain a supple yet upright body, well aligned in a straight vertical line. This can be more difficult than you expect, especially when you start bending your knees. Very often when people bend their knees their body alignment becomes distorted. Test yourself, standing side-on to a mirror. Don't look at the mirror, bend your knees and look at the mirror now. Is your back in a vertical line to the ground? A good way to keep a good alignment as you do this is to imagine you're going to sit on an empty chair, bending both your knees and hip joints. Practise it with the mirror and check yourself every now and then. We have found many people don't keep a good body alignment, but are not aware of it. That is why we said it is more difficult than expected. However once done right, your tai chi will improve greatly because qi flows best in an aligned body. Hunching forward will hinder the qi flow and compromise your balance and leaning backwards will create extra strain on the spine. So try to keep your body upright throughout all movements.

5. **Loosen or 'song' your joints.** You should relax when you do tai chi, but by relax we don't mean let your muscles go floppy. Instead, consciously and gently stretch your joints from within, almost like you're expanding your joints internally. Many people mis-translate the Chinese word 'song' as relaxation: song is both relaxed and loosened.

To practise loosening your upper limbs, form a semi-circle with your arms in front of your chest and imagine all your joints are stretching out gently from within. If you stretch out your shoulder joint this way, you should see a dimple at the middle of the shoulder joint.

To loosen the spine, imagine it's a piece of string, and that you're gently stretching it from both ends. For the lower limbs, bend your knees and stretch your hips out to form an arch as you crouch. Check in a mirror if your thighs are forming an arch. Other lower limb joints will gently expand from within.

6.   **Focus on your movements.** Imagine you are in a quiet and serene environment and your mind will also slow down, becoming quiet and serene. Keep yourself focused on practising your tai chi, your movements, breathing, balance and body alignment, and avoid any distraction.

Variation in speed of movements

Do your movements slowly without stopping. Make them continuous like water flowing in a river. Don't jerk. Maintain the same speed throughout.

At a more advanced level, controlling the speed of your movement relates to the evenness of the speed, rather than maintaining the same speed throughout. In Chen-style, when there is fastness intermixed with slowness, the force-delivering movements (fa jin) require a faster speed. Within all variations of speed in this style, there is evenness within them. This evenness within different speeds is the key to cultivating elasticity inside your force. In Yang and Sun-styles, where most movements appear to be at the same speed, at a closer examination, there are almost unperceivable differences in speed between parts of the movements.

> "The nature of all tai chi movements is essentially of alternating between gathering and delivering energy."

Classical texts by famous tai chi masters all say that at the end of each movement, there seems to be a point where you stop. However, there is in fact no stop. What this means in practice is that at this point there is a subtle variation of speed, which might seem to be a stop, but is not really so.

The nature of all tai chi movements is essentially of alternating between gathering and delivering energy. Breathing in is storing energy, as though you are drawing a bow, and breathing out is delivering energy, like shooting an arrow. At the end of the out breath there is a fa jin phase where the variation occurs. At the fa jin phase, the speed becomes faster. This particularly occurs in Chen-style tai chi. However in the softer styles like Yang and Sun, the difference is subtle, so subtle that is almost unperceivable. As soon as the force is delivered, the movement does not stop, it moves on in a curve, starting to gather energy. At the same time the speed slows down a fraction as though there is a stop. However, if there were a complete stop to the movement then the energy would stop as well. This would break the flow of energy and render tai chi less powerful. The continual flow of energy is a feature of tai chi. This variation of speed makes the transition between delivering and gathering of energy occur smoothly and enables it to continue.

At the beginner's stage, executing the same even speed throughout a movement trains you to control your mind and body coordination and integration. Later on this subtle variation of speed enhances your inner force.

When you are performing any movement, try to be conscious of storing energy and expressing it at the end of the movement at the same time as the variation of speed. For the softer styles like Yang and Sun, be sure to do it subtly. It is also important to be aware of not stopping; let the force bounce back up like the wave at the bottom of a curve, which smoothly and automatically moves upward in a curve to generate new force. This almost unperceivable variation of speed within one movement is the key to the regeneration of power. Think of the tai chi symbol: when yin thins out, the curve leads to yang, then complementary yin-yang energy causes the continuation of power.

In conclusion, after you have been through the phase of acquiring an evenness in your tai chi movements, a subtle variation of speed within a movement will help to improve your tai chi further. At the beginning of a movement, slow down subtly to gather energy and speed up a little to express the delivering of this energy, but take care to fully express the complete movement, not to cut it short and hurry into the next movement. At the same time, make sure you don't stop, so ensuring the continual flow of energy.

The four essential concepts

To significantly improve your tai chi, incorporate four essential concepts, **jing**, **song**, **chen**, and **huo**. These are an extension of the essential tai chi principles discussed in the previous section. The following repeats some of that information but explores it in different and deeper ways.

The four concepts complement each other, so you don't need to be completely proficient in one before moving on to another. They also affect each other positively, so that by learning more about one you will improve your understanding of the others. Try working on one concept for a period of at least a few weeks and then move on to another. But come back to each one regularly.

> "To significantly improve your tai chi, incorporate four essential concepts, **jing, song, chen,** and **huo.**"

Some of the concepts below might not immediately be clear to you. Don't let that concern you. As you progress further, you'll be able to understand them. In time, as your level of tai chi progresses, the words will take on a somewhat different meaning. Bear in mind that no one reaches perfection in all four concepts; progression is what matters. Remember to enjoy the progression. When I gain a deeper understanding of a principle that improves my tai chi, I feel like I have discovered new treasure.

Jing

Jing, roughly translated, means 'mental quietness' or 'serenity'. Think of the quietness in your mind from within. Imagine yourself in a quiet environment such as a tranquil rainforest; your mind is serene but you are still aware of the surroundings. As you practise tai chi, try to put yourself in that mental frame. A good way to help it is to focus on doing one movement at a time. Incorporate the essential principles in the previous section of this chapter, that is, control your movement, align your body, transfer your weight correctly and focus and loosen your joints with your movements. Work on one aspect at a time as well as putting your mind in the jing state. If you do this regularly, you'll become quiet from within and gradually be more aware of what your body is doing.

Attaining a certain degree of mental quietness will take time. But once you have achieved that certain degree, your mind will have a memory of that state. The next time you practise, you will be able to re-establish the same state of mind relatively quickly, so that you don't have to start again from scratch. As you practise more, you'll be able to move on to a higher level each time. A good way to help yourself come back to the same state is to use a key word. Near the end of your practice session, especially when you are in the jing state, think of the word 'jing' quietly to yourself. Then when you start the next practice session, saying the word jing again will help to take you to the state.

Jing improves relaxation and enhances mental focusing. This, in turn, relieves muscle tension and improves your coordination, making your tai chi practice more effective.

The mental quietness of tai chi is different from that of some forms of meditation where people are placed in a secluded environment and are oblivious of their surroundings. In the jing state, while you are serene from within, you are still aware of your environment and able to assess the situation around you at any time — a necessity when you are communicating with the environment (regardless of whether you are harmonising with the universe or facing an opponent, you are communicating with your surroundings). It is like having a small world within yourself and yet you are still in the bigger real world around you. Using the jing state will help you deal not only with a martial art fight but also with various crises in real life.

Song

Song is often translated as 'relaxation', but it means more than that in Chinese. It is relaxing, but it also conveys a sense of loosening and stretching out. Imagine all your joints loosening, or stretching out, or expanding gently from within. Take your shoulder joint, for example. If you gently stretch out that joint, you'll feel a small dimple on the top of the shoulder. If you tense the shoulder joint, the dimple disappears.

Now apply this technique to other joints. Visualise them loosening. For your upper limbs, loosen your elbows, wrists and finger joints by stretching them out from within in a gentle expansion. For the torso, the loosening should be vertical — visualise your spine as a piece of string that you gently stretch from both ends. For your lower limbs, form an arch as you crouch, stretching your hip joints and knee joints gently outwards.

This method of loosening constitutes a type of controlled relaxation, because when you gently stretch your joints, you're attaining song. When the body is in a song state, it releases the tension from stress. Song helps your qi flow better, builds internal strength and also improves flexibility. It will also enhance jing. The more your body develops song, the more your mind becomes jing, and as your mind becomes more jing, it further enhances song, and so setting up a positive cycle.

Chen

Chen (not the same word in Chinese as the name of the Chen-style of tai chi) means 'sinking'. You're probably already familiar with the term 'sinking your qi to the dan tian'. An area three-finger-widths below the belly button, the dan tian, is central to everything we do in tai chi.

Exhaling facilitates sinking qi to the dan tian, which in turn keeps your mind jing and loosens up your joints. You'll find using the dan tian breathing method will help you to feel the sensation of qi. This sensation differs from person to person, but for most, it's a warm, heavy feeling. As you breathe out, loosen your joints. You may feel a warm and heavy feeling in your dan tian. That's the feeling of sinking your qi. If you don't feel this initially, don't worry. Continue to practise the forms with your breathing coordinating with the movement, and be aware of your dan tian area as you exhale. As you progress, you'll eventually feel the qi in the dan tian and learn how to sink it there.

Chen enhances stability, song, and qi cultivation. Awareness of the dan tian will strengthen the internal structures of your body and improve your inner strength.

Huo

Huo means 'agility' or 'ability to move nimbly'. Being strong, having powerful qi and being in a good mental state are essential, and these attributes will be even more effective with better agility. Agility comes from regular practice with the proper body posture, weight transference, control of movements, loosened joints and strong internal strength. Agility aids qi cultivation and improves flexibility.

Dan tian breathing method

Correct breathing is the basis of gathering, storing and delivering energy, which plays a vital part in every tai chi movement. Below is my method of tai chi breathing, based on 30 years of experience as a medical doctor and tai chi practitioner. It is a powerful qi-building method to improve internal energy. It can be incorporated into all your tai chi movements. Remember that breathing and tai chi have a natural relationship; if you feel uncomfortable at any stage, let go and breathe naturally. When all movements are done right, the right breathing will usually happen.

The tai chi classics describe breathing as opening and closing. When you open, you're storing energy, just as when you draw an arrow in a bow. When you close, you're delivering energy, just as when you release and fire the arrow. Keeping this image in mind will help you understand the explanation below.

When you're inhaling (storing energy), think of taking life-energy into your body. When you exhale, think of delivering energy or force. This can be applied to all tai chi movements since all movements in all types of tai chi are, in essence, alternating opening and closing movements. For example, when your hands pull apart or when you're stepping forwards, that's an opening movement. In *Parting the Wild Horse's Mane*, Yang-style, as your hands are coming closer as though to carry a ball, you are storing your energy. Then, as you separate your hands, there's an out-breath and you're delivering energy. (Even though it looks like an opening movement, it is in fact a closing movement, as it associates with delivering force).

Up-and-down movements fit the same pattern. When you move your hands up, you're storing energy, and therefore you breathe in. When you bring your hands down, you're delivering energy (shooting the arrow) so you breathe out. Likewise when you stand up (in-breath) and bend down (out-breath).

Keep these images in mind whenever you're practising tai chi. When in doubt, focus on practising the form correctly — relax, loosen your joints and you'll find your breathing will most likely be correct. Don't force or hold your breath. Simply allow your body to breathe naturally.

Do this sitting or standing upright. Be aware of holding the correct posture. Put one hand on your abdomen just above the belly button and one hand beside your hip with your index and middle fingers just above the groin. Concentrate on your lower abdomen and the pelvic floor muscle.

When you inhale, expand your lower abdominal area (allow it to bulge out a little) and let your muscles relax. As you exhale, gently contract the pelvic floor muscles and the lower abdomen. Feel the contraction of the muscles with the index and middle fingers of your lower hand, keeping the area above your belly button still. Focus on contracting the pelvic floor muscles gently; so gently that it's almost like you're only thinking about it. Or imagine that you're contracting your pelvic floor muscles and bring them just half an inch closer to your belly button.

As you inhale and relax the pelvic and lower abdominal muscles, try not to relax them completely, but keep approximately 10-20 percent of the contraction.

As you do an open movement, inhale. Feel the expansion in the lower abdomen. Then as you do a close movement, exhale with your lower abdomen contracting. You'll find most parts of your body move appropriately with your breathing, assisting the correct execution of the dan tian breathing. Remember to keep your upper abdomen still. This breathing method helps to sink your qi to the dan tian and to enhance your qi power.

Chapter 12
Learning from effective teachers

The articles in this chapter have been written over the last few years by advanced tai chi trainers who are also experts in different fields. They provide valuable insight into different aspects of what makes an effective teacher. The articles have either been written especially for this book or have been reprinted here with kind permission from the authors. If you wish to reproduce them, please contact the authors for permission.

Enrich your tai chi practice with imagery

By Dr Yanchy Lacska and Dr Paul Lam

Yanchy Lacska, MA, EdS is a psychologist and associate professor at the Northwestern Health Sciences University College of Acupuncture and Oriental Medicine. He is a long time student of Gin Foon Mark and Hong Liu. He is certified by Dr Lam to teach Tai Chi for Arthritis. He lives in Hudson, Wisconsin.

Dr Paul Lam is a family physician, teacher, author and creator of the Tai Chi for Arthritis program. He lives in Sydney, Australia.

Yanchy and Paul have been working together to bring the Tai Chi for Arthritis program to the Midwest USA and both have a vision of spreading knowledge about tai chi and qi gong as scientifically validated systems of helping people with arthritis and other chronic pain conditions.

Yanchy's personal experience

My first tai chi experience was as a student in a once per week community education class in a high school gymnasium. The teacher was Douglas Bowes, a long time student of TT Liang. I remember how much I enjoyed the class and how each week I felt like I was finally learning and memorizing the form. That is, until I got home. Each week I would leave the class excited to practice only to arrive at home and forget at least some of what we had been taught. It took me several weeks before I came to a realization that I might correct this situation by applying a technique that I had learned and used as a psychologist. I began to apply this technique to help resolve my frustrating dilemma.

This is what I began to do. At the end of each practice, I would walk to my car, sit behind the steering wheel and imagine myself doing the tai chi forms. After mentally going through the forms a few times, I would drive home and then practice the forms physically again. The technique I was using is known as active imagery. Active imagery is a means to mentally practice, to communicate our conscious intent. This is not a new process, even in the West. In the 1970s, professional golfer, Jack Nicklaus said that he never hit a shot without first imagining the perfect flight and flawless landing of the ball on the green. In the late 1980s, I was coaching my daughter's community youth basketball team. I remember an experiment I had the girls carry out during practice. I asked them to execute ten free throws each and count the number of baskets they made. Next I had them sit down, close their eyes, and imagine in detail, standing at the free throw line and preparing to shoot. I led them step by step through imagery culminating with the ball cleanly swooping through the net. Next I had them shoot ten free throws again. The percentage of baskets successfully completed improved dramatically for each and every girl on the team.

Modern research

Lao Tze says in the Tao te Ching 'Without going outside, you may know the whole world.' In a modern scientific equivalent, Harvard neuroscientist, Steven Kosslyn, has demonstrated that when people imagine things, the parts of their brains involved with the senses they are using in their imagining become active. When people imagine moving, the areas of the prefrontal motor cortex that instruct the body to move become active. The brain therefore, cannot easily distinguish between actually doing tai chi forms and imagining doing tai chi forms.

Dr Richard M Suinn of Colorado State University took the imagery process to a new level with the development of visuo-motor behavior rehearsal or VMBR. This process combines deep relaxation with vivid mental imagery of the skill to be learned. Researchers at Texas State University used this method in a study of students in a beginning karate class. The class was divided into two groups. One group received only karate training. The other group was taught VMBR along with the karate instruction. The class met two times per week for six weeks. At the end of the six weeks students were asked to complete an anxiety inventory before being tested on karate skills. They also used their new skills in sparring. The VMBR group reported less anxiety, scored better on the skills test and scored more points in sparring than the karate only group.

Dr Kate Lorig works with groups of people who have arthritis at Stanford University. She and her colleagues also teach a combination of relaxation with imagery. Participants imagine performing exercises or skills with their joints loose and pain free. Those who use this combination regularly report less pain and improved physical and psychological functioning. In addition they make only about half of the doctor visits that they made for their arthritis before using relaxation and imagery.

How to use imagery for your tai chi practise

The first step in using imagery effectively then is relaxation. Lao Tze said 'Empty yourself of everything, return to the source of stillness.' This is a good description of relaxation. There are many relaxation techniques to try. To begin deep relaxation, close your eyes and begin to breath using the diaphragm or belly. As you inhale, allow the belly (diaphragm) to naturally expand. As you exhale, draw the belly back in. This is called diaphragm or dan tian breathing in qi gong and tai chi practice.

Diaphragmic breathing methods

There are two commonly accepted methods of diaphragm breathing in tai chi. The first is abdominal breathing. In this method, imagine that air travels past your nose to the trachea or the breathing tube to fill up the lungs and then continues to travel down to fill up the abdomen. When this happens, as you imagine air traveling to the dan tian, your abdomen swells up as you breathe in. Breathing out would be the reverse. The abdominal muscle contracts flattening your abdomen as you breathe out. The breathing should be slow, even, and continuous and in the same tempo as your tai chi movement. Breathing should not be forced. If there is any feeling of discomfort then you should go back to normal breathing.

Reverse abdominal breathing is the second way. As you breathe in, the upper part of your abdomen swells up a little but the lower part of your abdomen contracts. As you breathe out, the upper part of your abdomen contracts and your lower abdomen swells up. Reverse abdominal breathing is generally regarded as the more advanced method and enables you to sink your qi to the dan tian and is especially effective for Chen-style Fa Jin (delivering force).

The next step

To begin, use the first method of abdominal breathing, often referred to as natural breathing. After several breaths, complete a mental body scan, working your way down from the top of your head. Relax any tension you feel in that part of the body each time you exhale. Continue this process until you mentally reach the bottom of your feet. There are many other relaxation methods you can read about, such as progressive muscle relaxation, systematically tensing and relaxing muscle groups, or autogenic training. Relaxation has benefits besides preparing you for your tai chi imagery work. Regular deep relaxation can reduce blood pressure and enhance the immune system. Research at the Menninger Clinic found that people who can achieve a state of deep relaxation often experience insight into problems they are working to resolve. This state can produce receptive imagery from the unconscious helping us to discover our needs and potential for problem solving.

Once your body is relaxed, your mind is calm and you are no longer thinking about that report due at work or school or what is for dinner, it is time to begin the imagery practice. In order to utilize imagery to the fullest you must first focus your attention on the skill you wish to enhance. In this situation, on your tai chi. Focus all of your attention on a clear and vivid image of yourself standing ready to begin your tai chi forms. If interfering thoughts or images enter your mind, take a deep breath and allow the image to pass by as you exhale. Then refocus on the tai chi image.

Imagery mechanics

Imagery should not be confused with visualization. Imagery, in fact, does not require visualization at all to be effective. The objective in using imagery to enhance tai chi play is not to see pretty pictures in your mind, but to pay attention, to be mindful, to train the bodymind. Imagery can utilize any or all of the senses. It certainly can include visual imagery, but may also include images of sounds, kinesthetic sensations, and even smells. I remember attending workshops during which the presenter guided us through a visualization experience for relaxation. I always felt frustrated because I could not 'see' anything with my eyes closed. The leader would be saying in a soft, soothing voice, 'You are walking along the beach and now you come to the shore. You see the blue sky and the white sand. The beautiful blue-green water beckons to you.' I found myself getting more tense instead of relaxed, thinking, 'Hey! I'm not even at the beach yet. Wait for me.' It was later during my training in clinical hypnosis that I began to experience imagery through my other senses. I discovered that while I couldn't see the beach, I could feel the warm sun and feel the sand between my toes.

Now that you have achieved a clear image of yourself standing and ready to begin your tai chi practice you can continue the active imagery practice. Imagine beginning the commencement form in vivid detail. Use your breath as you would when doing the form physically. Imagine the shifting of your weight and the gentle raising of your arms. Imagine what it feels like to take the first step of your form and how the body moves from the waist. Feel the transfer from substantial to insubstantial. Imagine completing the movements to perfection. Continue this detailed imagery for every form. When you have mentally rehearsed all of the forms, continue for a few minutes with relaxed dan tian breathing allowing the images to settle and become part of your being. After you have completed this imagery practice, practice the forms physically. It is interesting to practice the form once physically before your imagery work and then again after your imagery session. Notice how the form has changed. How does the experience of tai chi change?

Practical guides

Using imagery during your tai chi practice reinforces that the mind is the master and the body is to follow. The Tai Chi Classics say that the mind directs the body, so using imagery is one of the ways the mind can direct the body. We would like to use a movement to illustrate how you could use imagery to enhance your tai chi learning. We chose the 24 Forms (or Steps) Taijiquan because it is the best known

Tai Chi set with many standardised texts available. We will use the Movement 21, *Turn to Deflect Downwards, Parry and Punch.*

From the previous move, as you turn, imagine the transferring of weight without allowing your body to bob up. Keep your knees bent, transfer your weight to the left foot, and maintain your body upright without leaning to one side. Then as you move your right hand in an arch to the right, left hand in an arch to the left, turn the left toe 135 degrees towards the right and then transfer your weight gradually back to the left foot, keeping your body upright. As you transfer your weight back, continue to move your right arm in a curve downwards so that your right hand ends just in front of and below the armpit. As you do this clench the right hand into a fist with palm facing down. The left hand moves up gently to the left corner of the head to protect your head.

Lift the right foot up so your right foot touches down in front of the left foot, heel down first and with toes pointing outward. Continue to move gently, your left hand pressing down. As you do this, imagine an opponent coming towards you punching with his right fist. Your left hand blocks and pushes his right hand down and at the same time, you turn your waist slightly to drive a force that moves the right fist forward to punch your opponent's nose. Also at the same time your left foot kicks forward to your opponent's shin.

Shift your weight onto the right foot and continue to turn your body to the right. Your body directs your right fist around to the right side, moving in a curve, ending up with the right fist next to the right hip with the palm facing up. Imagine now your opponent has stepped back, and then steps forward to punch you again and, as your body swings around, your left hand reaches out to block his punch. At the same time, take a step forward with your left foot. In your imagination you have to keep remembering your body, your posture, the purpose of your move. This will help you to focus where the force is and to be in control of your movements.

Finally, as your left hand presses down your opponent's fist, your right fist moves above the left hand and punches toward the opponent.

Conclusion

For the mind to control the body, it also means that the mind is calm and has great clarity. When you are fighting, a clear and calm mind will prevail. This solo practice will not only help you to remember your movements, but also it can bring you a long way in integrating your body, mind and spirit.

© Dr Yanchy Lacska and Dr Paul Lam, 2001.

Ethics of tai chi teaching

By Stephanie Taylor, MD

Dr Stephanie Taylor is a physician specialising in women's health care in Monterey, California, USA. She is board-certified in obstetrics and gynaecology and has taken additional certifications in menopause and holistic medicine. She is a Master Trainer in Tai Chi for Arthritis and Tai Chi for Diabetes and is experienced in Aikido and Qigong.

What is ethics? The dictionary states that it is a system of moral principles, often defined by culture or professional subgroup. In years past, we would have called it the development of character. As tai chi teachers, we have much in common with ethics that govern relationships between teachers and students, between priests and their congregations and between doctors and their patients. We uniquely share properties with all three and I would like to explore each in turn.

We share the ethics of a teacher in that we have the duty to impart knowledge to the best of our ability. To that end, we need to strive to perfect our own practice and our skills at communicating our knowledge to our students. We need to follow a course of continuing education for ourselves and also to be open enough to continually learn from our students. We must be open to new teaching techniques and new approaches to learning. We are different from teachers in school settings in that they are usually significantly older than their students, so that issues of fraternization do not usually arise.

We share the ethics of a priest in that the study of tai chi can be intensely personal, particularly on an advanced level. Students often come to seek not only the physical skill but also a personal or spiritual transformation. The teacher is often elevated to a special status and is expected to embody the highest ethical and personal standards both in the teaching setting and in their personal life. Since this relationship is often one of equal ages, socialization as peers outside the teaching setting is likely to occur.

We share the ethics of physicians in that we observe several of the basic principles of beneficence (promoting good), non-maleficence (avoiding doing harm) and veracity (truthfulness). We are in a fiduciary or protective relationship with a student who is often dependent on us for their 'tai chi wellbeing'.

So how do we achieve these lofty goals? Perhaps the best approach is the old adage, 'Know Thyself'. You should recognize your own abilities and limitations as well as your reactions to individual students. It is natural for students to think highly of their teacher, they usually select a teacher based on a favorable reputation and an expectation of a high level of performance as a practitioner and as a human being. That is an excellent start, and it is important that we understand and gratefully accept this appreciation, but not let it affect our teaching practice. The familiar adage is to 'Not take yourself too seriously'. The psychological concept is called 'transference'. Transference refers to feelings of the client toward the therapist. Counter transference refers to feelings of the therapist toward the client. Both are useful and in many cases essential for a healing relationship. The problem comes when these things take on a life of their own, and that happens because one person or both is unaware of what is happening. Since we are the teachers it is our responsibility to be aware of these issues and manage them.

For example, a transference issue could occur when a student unconsciously identifies the teacher with a bullying father, and collapses in tears when given gentle corrections. A counter transference problem for the teacher would classically be taking the adulation seriously, developing an inflated self of him or herself and taking sexual or financial advantage of a student.

In summary, we have a duty to our students to be the best we can be professionally as well as to look after their interests, even though they may resist. You do not have to be a psychologist, but remember that being caring and compassionate as a principle will get you through many difficult situations.

© Stephanie Taylor, MD, 2004.

'Do unto others ...'

By Pat Webber

Patricia Webber is a senior instructor at Better Health Tai Chi Chuan in Sydney, Australia. Pat is a retired teacher who has trained extensively with Dr Paul Lam. She has given talks and lectures and has also taught tai chi interstate and overseas.

What does effective teaching mean? The Macquarie dictionary says that 'effective' means 'producing the intended or expected result'.

What result do we expect when we start teaching a tai chi class? Is it that after a certain amount of time our students will be able to complete a routine independently? This is no mean feat, and for some students, that is as far as their interest goes. I think for most instructors, however, the intended result is that their students become aware that there is something more to tai chi than learning a set routine.

So, for me effective teaching means that I have given some foundation for others to begin their own journey of discovery into tai chi as well as the desire to do this.

Having had personal experiences of poor teaching in the past, experiences that have killed my initial interest in a number of subjects, has made me aware of the old saying 'Do unto others as you would have them do unto you.' With this in mind, I made a random list of what I really want in a teacher.

I'll begin with the most basic things.

Start on time

What does this have to do with effective teaching? Well, it sets the tone for the session and shows that the instructor is professional and serious in his/her approach. If I have paid for an hour's teaching, that's what I expect to get. To develop this good habit requires **Practice**.

Be seen and be heard

Have you ever been in a class where you've not been able to hear what's being said or to see what the instructor is doing because he/she never moves from the one spot or spends the session with his/

her back to you? I've been in such a class. The instructor could have been saying his rosary or peeling an orange for all I could see or hear. **Practise** speaking to the person at the back and practise positioning yourself to be seen.

Learn names

I like to be acknowledged by name. This helps me to feel more at ease. This needs **Patience** and **Perseverance** and **Practice** on the part of the instructor and perhaps name tags.

Prepare

The instructor may perform a move well, but does that mean that he/she can teach it effectively? Not necessarily. Each move needs to be broken down into several parts that can be taught individually, each new little part being joined on to the preceding part. Proceed from the known to the unknown. This preparation requires time, **Patience** and **Practice** on the part of the instructor.

Tell me again

I have read of Professor Cheng Man-ch'ing, 'He would tell you something once, perhaps twice, but if you persisted in the error, for whatever reason, he gave up. Perhaps something would snap you out of it; there was always that possibility. But he was too busy to waste time with you.' No doubt, the professor was operating on a different level to most people, but I need my instructor to be **Patient**.

Give me some personal attention

It's very easy to give a lot of attention to the more outgoing personalities in a group. This can happen without the instructor really being aware of it. It's also tempting to give extra attention to somebody who shows more potential than the rest. Everybody wants to feel that they are worthy of some of the instructor's time. **Practice** giving equal attention to all students.

Look for the good

Unfortunately, it is always easier to find fault than to see the good, both in ourselves and in others. If I'm struggling with some move, I don't need somebody else to tell me I'm making a complete hash of it. But, if I'm reassured that I have some part of it right, then at least I have something to build on. But I don't want to be patronised. The comments should be honest. **Practise** looking for those good points.

Modify

There are some moves that I will never be able to do for various reasons, but I appreciate being either given a modification or being reassured that my own modification is true to the spirit of tai chi. This requires **Practice** on the part of the instructor as well as **Perseverance** in extending their own knowledge so as to advise me in this matter.

See what I'm doing

Don't just look at me with a mind in neutral. How often have you watched somebody perform a move and felt that it's just not right? In order to help the student, the instructor has to be able to analyse the move. This **Practice** of analysing movements should start with preparation for classes and also be used in our own practice. **Practise** engaging the mind as well as the body.

Credibility

I want to feel that my instructor knows what he/she is talking about. To gain knowledge and skill to pass on to others requires **Patience**, **Perseverance** and **Practice**.

Enthusiasm

I want to feel stimulated by the feeling that the instructor has for this subject. I know that teaching the same thing for the umpteenth time can become a drag if the instructor allows that to happen. So, I want my instructor to introduce some variety that will keep both of us interested. Again, this needs **Practice**.

I think every person could make their own list of what they want in a teacher. That will help them to develop their skills and encourage them to keep trying.

© Pat Webber, 2006.

Letting go of tai chi

By Shelia Rae

Shelia Rae is dedicated to sharing and promoting the study of qigong and tai chi worldwide. She has been teaching Tai Chi for Arthritis since 1999 and holds classes at the University of Memphis and the University of Mississippi as well as in churches, retirement homes, rehabilitation centers etc. In 2003, at an international competition held in Dallas, Texas, she was awarded both Gold (Sun-style) and Bronze (Yang-style) medals. Sheila is affiliated with The Healing Arts Medical Group of Memphis where she is a medical qigong instructor and Acupuncture Detoxification Specialist licensed in the State of Tennessee.

The very act of letting go implies that we are in possession of a thing. When we apply this concept to tai chi, we understand that without learning and practicing the form, we do not possess tai chi awareness. But this awareness is not a product of perfected moves and steps only. While good form is vital to the overall experience, it is not the end goal for the serious practitioner.

There comes a point in our practice where we must learn to let go of the form, the perfectionism, and the ego. As we begin tai chi, the ego is good because it helps us to see what we can achieve. It is powerful, fun, and exciting. But like anything we practice to learn, eg, piano, dance, even cooking, there comes a time when we must let go of trying to follow the prescribed pattern and let the art move through our souls.

We must ask ourselves what is our purpose in learning tai chi. We learn form to become formless; to integrate mind, body, and spirit. We learn the principles of tai chi to become accountable to ourselves, not to judge others, but to teach by example how tai chi extends beyond the physical form. When we can use the principles of tai chi to let go and flow in all our activities, we naturally begin to influence our tai chi practice.

If we constantly train to perfect the moves of tai chi, we can't realize the true bliss of doing tai chi. When we let go of the form, wonderful connections can happen. First the moves connect together effortlessly, and then we can connect to the true essence of blending with our environment, with others, and with the universe itself.

I urge you to release the exactness in order to embrace the wholeness that is tai chi.

Effective teaching is building community

By Professor Russell Smiley, PhD

Professor Russell Smiley is a Tai Chi for Arthritis Master Trainer in the Minneapolis/St Paul area of the USA. He is a health educator and has been on the health faculty at Normandale Community College in Bloomington, Minnesota for the last 18 years, where he has developed the curriculum for and currently teaches courses on tai chi, healing qigong, and stress management. In 2006 he was presented with their Distinguished Faculty Award for a faculty member (voted by graduating students) who has made the greatest impact on students during their college career at Normandale.

Ultimately, when we have a successful tai chi class we have created a safe space where the participants have formed a common bond around tai chi, developed a connection with you and other students, and formed a community. Teaching is working with people.

Having gone through the formal graduate school educational experience to 'become' a teacher, I played the game and emerged with graduate degrees and pieces of paper that implied that I could teach. The simple formula to create a teacher was learning theories, memorizing lectures and book knowledge, practicing teaching, playing with simulations, and doing research. On paper it looked good. In reality there was a big void in knowing about the big picture, how to connect from the heart with students and colleagues, and how to nurture myself on this mystical journey. Having the best skills and knowledge from higher education did not guarantee my success as a teacher. Practice and experience taught me that there is much, much more to be learned — and this comes from truly connecting with people and forming communities.

At the June 2006 Tai Chi Workshop (held at St Mary's of the Woods College, Terre Haute, Indiana) we formed a community with old and new friends who all brought a similar desire and passion to learn tai chi. Dr Lam has held the big picture for over 10 years and has traveled the world sharing his dream. As Master Trainers, Senior Trainers, Instructors, and tai chi players, we believe in his mission. Many of us teach his model to others, while others embrace the contribution of tai chi to the health and betterment of others. Regardless, we are all members of an ever-growing community, which circles the globe.

Wherever we go, we build community. It requires us to embrace others, connect with our students, and learn about ourselves. We form intimate communities with spouses and significant others, colleagues, family and close friends. These relationships need to be cultivated and nurtured. Our friends from this conference can help us learn and grow. I advocate keeping in touch throughout the year with an email, telephone call, or a meeting over tea. Share your successes and challenges and stay connected. Build a support team with other Tai Chi for Arthritis, Tai Chi for Diabetes or Tai Chi for Back Pain instructors. This experience called life on planet earth is meant to be shared with those we care about and who care about us.

My students are my best teachers. They make what I do possible. They challenge me. They make me look at life from another perspective. They keep bringing me back to the present time. This is what Caroline Demoise calls the 'beginners mind'.

In your classes honor each individual's learning process and purpose for being in your class. Listen with your ears, eyes and heart. Encourage feedback from students and other teachers so that you can stay engaged. Play tai chi with a purpose and make it fun and exciting. Bring an open heart, enthusiasm, and a big smile to class. Throw a surprise birthday party, bring tea or treats. Make the tai chi class fun and memorable. Greet each person in every class, and build rapport. Realize that you may not always have the answer (and may need to acknowledge such) but be willing to find the information. Know that sometimes life takes students away from tai chi, and this is not a reflection on you. Remember that no person can change another without their permission. All we can do is to give students wings, and encourage them to fly. Empower each individual in class to be the best that they can possibly be.

The third component of building community is embracing and nurturing your own body, mind and spirit. This is the one aspect of teaching effectively which is sadly overlooked in many formal educational training programs. Who is more intimately qualified to know you than you? Pat Lawson said we are given a map, but we have the power to determine how we get there.

Learn to nurture and love yourself. Stay engaged in your process by reading, writing, taking classes, meditating, practicing tai chi, etc — whatever fills your glass, bubbles your qi, and gives you passion. Life is an adventure.

As Cynthia Fels says, know your learning style, as well as knowing how to recognize this in others, and use your learning style strengths in your self-care.

Realize that there is no right answer, but a multitude of possibilities that can be explored. Learn about how you manage conflict. Perhaps there are other ways of approaching a situation other than being confrontational? Can you separate your stuff from what is really happening? If it is a repeating situation, maybe you have something to learn?

Stay amused. Laugh at yourself. Find the humor in each situation. Laughter keeps you light, reduces tensions, releases joy juice (endorphins), and helps you to more easily keep moving through your process. When I get stuck and have difficulty finding amusement, my wife's favorite saying comes to mind: **'I can't wait to see how this turns out to be perfect!'** — and it has always turned out perfect for my life. In hindsight, everything has its perfection.

As human beings, we walk upright with our feet grounded on the earth and our head suspended from the heavens. We greet others with open arms and an open heart. This was no accident. We are designed to engage and connect with one another. Teaching Tai Chi is connecting people and building community on a global scale.

© Professor Russell Smiley, 2006.

Appendix: Samples and resources

Sample feedback form

Your feedback helps us to teach better!

Which classes did you do? _____

How did you find out about the classes? _____

What did you wish to achieve from attending the classes?

_____

_____

_____

Have you achieved your goal?
(1 = No; 3 = Some of it; 5 = Yes, everything!)

1   2   3   4   5

How do you rate your classes overall?
(1 = poor; 3 = fair; 5 = excellent)

Content:	1	2	3	4	5
Method of teaching:	1	2	3	4	5
Organisation:	1	2	3	4	5
The venue:	1	2	3	4	5

What did you like most about the classes?

_____

_____

_____

Would you change any part of the classes?

_____

_____

_____

Would you like to come back to our next term of classes?
Yes ☐ No ☐

If the answer is yes, what would you be interested in doing next time? (Any suggestions are welcome, including classes not offered currrently.)

_____

_____

_____

Do you know anyone who might be interested in coming to our classes? If you'd like to give us their name and contact details we'll let them know next time we're running new classes.

_____

_____

_____

Sample release form

*A suggested release form only — subject to the approval of
your own legal professional.*

Tai Chi For Arthritis Workshop

Date of workshop _____

Location of workshop _____

Acknowledgement of Personal
Responsibility/Consent

I understand that Tai Chi is a gentle exercise which may enhance my physical fitness and improve my condition. I confirm that my physical condition is fit to safely participate in this workshop.

In consideration for admission to this workshop (a) I hereby accept full responsibility for and assume the risk of any injuries sustained because of my participation in this workshop or practice or lessons involving Tai Chi and (b) I hereby release and hold harmless Tai Chi Productions, its respective officers, directors and shareholders, the instructors and all personnel in association with the Tai Chi Workshop for any liabilities, injuries and expenses which may arise as a result of participation in this workshop or practice or lessons involving Tai Chi.

I consent to the use of any photographs or videos taken of me, as well as any feedback or written comments by me in connection with the Tai Chi Workshop, for publicity, promotion, demonstration or other business purposes, in any medium, including the internet, and I waive any right to compensation in connection with such use.

Signature of workshop participant _____

Full Name _____

Sample enrolment form and waiver

You can use this text to create an enrolment form for students of your tai chi classes. Adapt it as required for your purposes.

Better Health Tai Chi Chuan

Participant to complete:

Name _____

Date of Birth _____

Address _____

Telephone: (H) _____ (W) _____

Contact person in case of emergency:

_____

Telephone: (H) _____ (W) _____

Program Guidelines

Classes are open to any suitable person as specified in our brochure, provided they are medically fit, are independently mobile and can participate without assistance in the class.

Any participant who has any doubt whether they are medically fit to attend the class, is required to have a medical clearance from their doctor prior to commencing.

Classes usually last for one hour. Participants are encouraged to have a rest in between if needed and to work within their own comfort zone at all times.

Participants are required to do a gentle warm-up exercise before they start and cooling-down exercise before finishing.

Accredited instructors conduct classes.

The Tai Chi exercise in this program would be similar to walking in terms of physical exertion.

Waiver

I have read the Program Guidelines and I understand that there is an inherent risk in any exercise activities and I agree to abide by the rules set out in the Guidelines.

I know that there are no medical reasons why I should not participate in this class or workshop. I understand if I do have any medical reasons why I should not participate in this class or workshop then it is my responsibility to obtain a clearance from my doctor before commencing.

Signature _____

Date _____

For Instructor's Use Only

Notes _____

Signature _____

Date _____

Sample brochure

A brochure is essential to promote your tai chi class. You can do this easily with any word processing program. The instructions below are for Microsoft Word and are for a three fold brochure made from a one page document, that will fit easily into a standard (DL) envelope.

When you are writing your text, bear in mind the most important thing is to tell your readers (potential students) what benefits your tai chi class can offer them. You can use all or some of the suggested text below, but please check everything and modify it for your own needs.

To make a one-page 3-fold brochure in Microsoft Word

Step 1: Go to File/page setup, and then select your paper size, (letter size for USA and A4 for other countries), and also select landscape format. Click OK

Step 2: Go to Format/column and select 3 columns. Then adjust the width to suit you. Make them about 7 cms.

Step 3: Insert your text in the appropriate column.

Always print it out, fold it to make sure it is laid out correctly and read everything carefully before you get it printed in large numbers. It is a good idea to ask as many friends as possible to check it for you.

Suggested text for your brochure

(Your front page – the 3rd column of the first page)

(A picture: preferably with several people (about the same age and sex of the students you want to recruit) looking happy doing the Tai Chi for Arthritis forms you will be teaching.)

Tai Chi for Arthritis

Certified Instructor: *(Your name)*

Tai Chi for Arthritis is a program composed by Dr Paul Lam especially for people with arthritis. It has been shown by scientific studies to be effective and safe and is supported by many arthritis foundations.

(On first page when you open up the brochure)

What is Tai Chi?

Tai chi originated from ancient China. Nowadays it is practised throughout the world as an exercise for better health. Many scientific studies have proven that it is amazingly effective for health. Tai chi:

- is suitable for almost anyone
- relieves pain and improves quality of life for people with arthritis
- relieves stress and improves concentration
- integrates body and mind

Why do Tai Chi?

Tai chi is fun, can be easy to learn and improves your health and quality of life.

Comments from participants

(You can replace these with your own or get up-to-date ones from the Forum at www.taichiproductions.com.)

"... Tai chi has given me the space in which to move my body slowly whilst calming my mind." (Betty, 79 years of Marrickville)

"Pain in my knees... each time I come to the class I experience an easing of the level of pain and I can move around more freely for the rest of the day." (Pat, 55 years of Balmain)

(On the back pages)

How does Tai Chi work?

Health and exercise experts advise that an exercise program for people with arthritis should incorporate exercises that improve muscular strength, flexibility, and fitness. Tai chi is proven to improve all of these components, as well as having additional health benefits. Tai chi improves relaxation, balance, posture, and immunity.

- Muscle strength is important for supporting and protecting joints, which will reduce pain.
- Flexibility exercises also help to reduce pain and stiffness, enabling you to move easier.
- Fitness or stamina is important for overall health and proper function of your heart, lungs, and muscles.
- Tai chi facilitates the flow of Qi through your body. Qi is the life energy that circulates throughout the body, performing many functions to maintain good health. Practising tai chi helps to strengthen your Qi, therefore improving your health.

Tai Chi for Arthritis — the Program

There are many forms of tai chi but a specially designed program has many advantages. Dr Lam's team of tai chi and medical experts has created a simple, safe and effective program for arthritis. Many people have enjoyed learning the program and have gained significant health benefits. The program has been proven by scientific studies to improve pain, quality of life and balance.

Arthritis foundations in many countries including USA, UK and Australia, support this program. For more information contact your local arthritis foundation or visit Dr Lam's website (www. taichiforarthritis.com).

About your instructor (Your name)

(A short biography listing your special interests and credentials. Be brief and focus on what you can do to help your potential students.)

Dates and times

Cost

Clothing

Participants should wear loose comfortable clothes and flat shoes suitable for exercise.

For more information

(Insert your contact details including phone numbers, address, email address etc.)

http://www.taichiforarthritis.com

Sample letter to a newspaper

<Nancy Kaye's name and contact details>
<Newspaper's address>
<Date>

Dear <Contact's name>

I'm probably the only one in the Bay Area of Northern California who is teaching a new and special form of Tai Chi for people with arthritis. Called Tai Chi for Arthritis (TCA) and developed by Paul Lam, a family physician in Sydney, Australia, this form consists of gentle stretches and relaxing movements designed specifically to alleviate some of the discomfort associated with arthritis as well as improve general health.

Before I go any further, I want to assure you that I'm not selling myself or seeking financial gain. I'm simply seeking heightened awareness of this unique exercise program in hope that it can provide help for the one in seven members of our community who suffer from arthritis.

Last spring, I received certification to teach TCA after completing a workshop in Southern California given by Dr. Lam. I had been teaching 'regular' Tai Chi at Pleasant Hill Education Center (Mt Diablo Adult Education) for several years and last fall, in cooperation with the Arthritis Foundation, added classes in TCA. I also taught the form at Rossmoor.

At present, I'm teaching two sections of Tai Chi for Arthritis at the Pleasant Hill center. Since part of the funding comes from the state, the cost to the student is minimal.

The enclosed tape is of the Dr Dean Edell Show, which is shown nationally on ABC. This segment, about a minute and a half long, aired on 12/20/00. The producer of the Dean Edell segments wanted to do a show on how Tai Chi benefits arthritis. She got my name from the Arthritis Foundation. She asked me to furnish one of my students for an interview. You'll see her — Concord resident Robin Malby, who has fibromyalgia — on the tape. You'll also see Dr Paul Lam.

I hope you will consider Tai Chi for Arthritis for a feature story. I think it would not only interest your readers but benefit many of them as well.

Thank you.

Nancy Kaye

Sample letter to a television show

<My name and contact details>
<*Today Show*'s address>
<Date>

Dear <Contact's name>

Re: Tai Chi for Arthritis telecast on the Today Show
(14th January 99) from Good Morning America

Thank you for broadcasting the interview I did with Dr Snyderman of *Good Morning America*. The interview has generated many inquiries. Although your program did not broadcast my contact number, I received telephone calls from many motivated people.

Most of the queries were: Why is Tai Chi beneficial for arthritis? What does it look like? And how can we get more information?

When I viewed the segment on the *Today Show*, I had two concerns. Firstly, some of these questions were not answered. Secondly, because it was an American program the producer of *Good Morning America* found several groups of Tai Chi practitioners from the USA to demonstrate the program.

I am an Australian living in Sydney, I wonder if your show would like to do a follow up interview with me? Judging from the number of telephone calls I received, there appears to be much interest in Tai Chi for Arthritis, and I can bring an Australian group to demonstrate this program.

I have been working closely in association with the Arthritis Foundations throughout Australia to train instructors. If you were to interview my team, we can provide your viewers with information on how to find a suitable form of Tai Chi for their condition through Arthritis Foundations.

Please contact me if you feel this is worthy of your support.

Yours faithfully,

Dr Paul Lam

Sample press release

(Insert your contact details clearly at the top of the press release.)

Subject: Tai Chi for Diabetes study

One in four Australians either suffers from diabetes or pre-diabetes, with the incidence of diabetes increasing, not only in Australia, but in the entire western world.

It is particularly significant then, that the Royal Australian College of General Practitioners has approved a grant to study the effectiveness of exercise, specifically tai chi, to improve diabetes management and reduce the risk of heart disease.

This study is administered by the St George Division of General Practice and is led by Dr Paul Lam, a general practitioner from Narwee who is also a world leader in the field of tai chi for health improvement. The co-authors are: Associate Professor Terry Diamond, Director of the Diabetic Clinic at St George Hospital and Professor Nick Zwar and Dr Sarah Dennis, from the University of NSW.

The research team is looking for volunteers to participate in the study. The participants will get free tai chi lessons for 3 or 6 months, and will be contributing most significantly to the world's first diabetes and tai chi study. Participants must have had Type II diabetes for more than six months, and be having some problem controlling the condition. They must be over 30-years-old, have no medical reasons to stop them from doing gentle exercise, and be willing to participate in tai chi classes for up to six months. The classes will start in early March this year.

Tai Chi is an enjoyable exercise and should improve diabetes control. Studies have shown tai chi to be effective in improving hypertension, cardiovascular fitness, muscle strength, balance and to relieve stress. It makes good rational sense that tai chi should also improve diabetes. We know it works, but we need your help to prove it. Your help will make more people aware of how tai chi can help them improve their diabetes.

To participate or for more information ring our research project manager xxx at phone xxx.

Resources

Books

Bandura, Albert, *Self-efficacy: The Exercise of Control*, WH Freeman and Company, New York, 1997.

Covey, Stephen, *The Seven Habits of Highly Effective People*, Simon and Schuster, New York, 1990.

Csikszentmihalyi, Mihaly, *Finding Flow, the Psychology of Engagement with Everyday Life*, Basic Books, New York 1997.

Donovan, Grant; McNamara, Jane and Gianoli, Peter, *Exercise Danger: 30 exercises to avoid plus 100 safer and more effective alternatives*, A Wellness Australia Publication, Western Australia 1988.

Goleman, Daniel, *Emotional Intelligence*, Bantam Books, New York 1994.

Goleman, Daniel, *Working with Emotional Intelligence*, Bloomsbury Publishing, London, 1998.

Harris, Thomas, *I'm OK, you're OK*, Harper Paperbacks, New York, 2004.

Kircher, Pamela M, MD *Love is the Link*, Larson Publications, New York 1995.

Lam, Paul, and Horstman Judith, *Overcoming Arthritis*, Dorling Kindersley, Sydney, 2002.

Lam, Paul and Kaye, Nancy, *Tai Chi for Beginners and the 24 Forms*, Limelight Publications, Sydney, 2006.

George Leonard, *Mastery — The Keys to Success and Long-term Fulfilment*, Plume Books, New York, 1991.

Pyke, Frank S, (ed) *Better Coaching* — Advanced coach's manual published by Australian Sports Commission.

Magazines

T'ai Chi (The International Magazine of T'ai Chi Chuan)
Wayfarer Publications
P.O. Box 39938
Los Angeles
CA 90039-0938
USA
Phone: (323) 665 7773
Email: taichi@tai-chi.com

Qi (The Journal of Traditional Eastern Health and Fitness)
Insight Publishing Inc
P.O. Box 18476
Anaheim Hills
CA 92817
USA
Phone: 714 779 1796
Email: editor@qi-journal.com

Tai Chi Associations

Tai Chi Association of Australia, working together to promote tai chi in Australia.

www.taichiaustralia.com

Tai Chi for Health Community, a non profit organisation dedicated to bringing tai chi to as many people as possible for health improvement.

www.taichiforhealthcommunity.org

Tai Chi America, provides a multimedia learning resource and archive for all those interested in tai chi chuan and chi kung.

www.taichiamerica.com

Tai Chi Union, the largest collective of independent tai chi chuan instructors in the British Isles.

www.taichiunion.com

Better Health Tai Chi Chuan Inc, an Australian non-profit organisation dedicated to providing an ideal environment for all members to grow through tai chi.

www.betterhealthtcc.com.au

Websites

Dr Paul Lam's website — Tai Chi Productions

www.taichiproductions.com

This website contains tai chi information, discussions, lists of tai chi instructors worldwide, and up-to-date products from Dr Paul Lam's team.

Tai Chi Productions is dedicated to improving people's health and quality of life by promoting Dr Paul Lam's Tai Chi for Health Programs through research, education and instructional material.

World Tai Chi & Qigong Day

www.worldtaichiday.org

The biggest event in tai chi worldwide.

DVD/Videos

Tai Chi Productions

www.taichiproductions.com

Dr Paul Lam's team of experts has produced several series of tai chi DVD/videos, from introductory teach-yourself series for health, to intermediate and advanced series to expand your skill. The most popular titles are:

Tai Chi for Arthritis (DVD in English, Chinese, French, Spanish, German and Italian)

Tai Chi for Osteoporosis

Tai Chi for Diabetes

Tai Chi for Older Adults

Tai Chi 4 Kidz

Tai Chi for Beginners (DVD in English, Chinese, French, Spanish, German and Italian)

Qigong for Health
Tai Chi — the 24 Forms
The 32 Forms Tai Chi Sword.
The 42 Forms
The 42 Sword Forms
Tai Chi Music CD

For more information and to buy these products online, go to the website:

www.taichiproductions.com

Contact Dr Paul Lam for more information about the intermediate and advanced series.

Notes

Chapter 1: Why teach tai chi?

1   Pamela M. Kircher, MD, *Love is the Link*, A hospice doctor shares her experience of near-death and dying, Larson Publications, New York 1995.

2   Chenchen Wang, MD, MSc; Jean Paul Collet, MD, PhD; Joseph Lau, MD, *The effect of tai chi on health outcomes in patients with chronic conditions, a systematic review*, Archives of Internal Medicine, JAMA, 2004; 164:493–501.

3   GF Fuller, *Falls in the elderly*, American Family Physician, 2000 Apr 1; 61(7): 2159–68, 2173–4.

4   Raymond Cripps and Judy Carman, *Falls by the elderly in Australia: Trends and data for 1998*, Australian Institute of Health and Welfare, Canberra, 2001.

Chapter 2: What it takes to be an effective teacher

1   R Song, Eo Lee, P Lam, SC Bae, *Effects of tai chi exercise on pain, balance, muscle strength, and perceived difficulties in physical functioning in older women with osteoarthritis: A randomized clinical trial*, Journal of Rheumatology, 2003; 30(9): 2039–44.

   JH Choi, JS Moon and R Song, *The effects of Sun-style tai chi exercise on physical fitness and fall prevention in fall-prone adults*, Journal of Advanced Nursing, 2005, 51(2), 150–157.

2   The Tai Chi for Arthritis workshop consists of supplied teaching materials for individual preparation beforehand, two days' face-to-face instruction, a final test and regular updates. Suitable health professionals and tai chi practitioners who have fulfilled the requirements are certified to teach this simple program. The program aims to help people improve their health in general and it is especially safe and suitable for people with arthritis. These workshops have enjoyed great success as attested to by

many thousands of healthier arthritis sufferers worldwide, as well as by several published studies to date of results gained by instructors trained from these workshops.

3   Grant Donovan, Jane McNamara and Peter Gianoli, *Exercise Danger: 30 exercises to avoid plus 100 safer and more effective alternatives*, a Wellness Australia Publication, Western Australia 1988.

4   Frank S Pyke, ed, *Better Coaching* — Advanced coach's manual published by Australian Sports Commission.

5   I have created a 3-step set of safe warm-up and cooling-down exercises that you can use without applying for copyright. These exercises are described briefly in Chapter 8 and are also available in my detailed instructional DVD *Tai Chi for Beginners* and the book *Tai Chi for Beginners and the 24 Forms*.

6   The essential tai chi principles for beginners are outlined in Chapter 11.

7   George Leonard, *Mastery — The Keys to Success and Long-term Fulfilment*, Plume Books, New York, 1991.

8   Stephen Covey, *The Seven Habits of Highly Effective People*, Simon and Schuster, New York, 1990.

9   Daniel Goleman, *Working with Emotional Intelligence*, Bloomsbury Publishing, London, 1998.

10   Daniel Goleman, *Emotional Intelligence*, Bantam Books, New York 1994

11   Thomas Harris, *I'm OK, you're OK*, Harper Paperbacks, New York, 2004.

12   Paul Lam and Nancy Kaye, *Tai Chi for Beginners and the 24 Forms*, Limelight Publications, Sydney, 2006.

13   Albert Bandura, *Self-efficacy: The Exercise of Control*, WH Freeman and Company, New York, 1997.

14   Mihaly Csikszentmihalyi, *Finding Flow, the Psychology of Engagement with Everyday Life*, Basic Books, New York 1997.

Chapter 3: How do you know that you are an effective teacher?

1   George Leonard, Mastery, *The Keys to Success and Long-term Fulfilment*, Plume Books, New York, 1991.

Chapter 4: Safety first

1   Associations including: American College of Sports Medicine (www.acsm.org); American Council on Exercise (www.acefitness.org) and Sport Medicine Australia (www.sma.org.au).

2   Grant Donovan, Jane McNamara and Peter Gianoli, *Exercise Danger: 30 exercises to avoid plus 100 safer and more effective alternatives*, a Wellness Australia Publication, Western Australia 1988.

Chapter 5: The Stepwise Progressive Teaching Method

1   Albert Bandura, *Self-efficacy: The Exercise of Control*, WH Freeman and Company, New York, 2003.

2   A movement here is synonymous with a form. A set of tai chi consists of many forms or movements, for example the 24 Forms has 24 movements and the 12-movement Tai Chi for Arthritis set has 12 forms. Within a movement there are several parts. For example the *Single Whip* movement in Tai Chi for Arthritis can be divided into three parts (but of course you can divide it into as many parts as appropriate for the situation).

3   Dr Paul Lam and Nancy Kaye, *Tai Chi for Beginners and the 24 Forms*, Limelight Press, Sydney, 2006.

Chapter 10: Collaborating with research studies

1   Song R, Lee EO, Lam P, Bae SC, *Effects of tai chi exercise on pain, balance, muscle strength, and perceived difficulties in physical functioning in older women with osteoarthritis: A randomized clinical trial.* Journal of Rheumatology, 2003, 30(9), pp. 2039–44.

2   Choi JH, Moon JS and Song R, *The effects of Sun-style tai chi exercise on physical fitness and fall prevention in fall-prone adult.* Journal of Advanced Nursing, 2005, 51(2), pp. 150–157.